INTERNATIONAL
WILDLIFE
ENCYCLOPEDIA

THIRD EDITION

Volume 5

CRA–DUC

Marshall Cavendish Corporation
99 White Plains Road
Tarrytown, New York 10591–9001

Website: www.marshallcavendish.com

© 2002 Marshall Cavendish Corporation

Library of Congress Cataloging-in-Publication Data

Burton, Maurice, 1898-
    International wildlife encyclopedia / [Maurice Burton, Robert Burton] .-- 3rd ed.
        p. cm.
    Includes bibliographical references (p.).
    Contents: v. 1. Aardvark - barnacle goose -- v. 2. Barn owl - brow-antlered deer -- v. 3. Brown bear - cheetah -- v. 4. Chickaree - crabs -- v. 5. Crab spider - ducks and geese -- v. 6. Dugong - flounder -- v. 7. Flowerpecker - golden mole -- v. 8. Golden oriole - hartebeest -- v. 9. Harvesting ant - jackal -- v. 10. Jackdaw - lemur -- v. 11. Leopard - marten -- v. 12. Martial eagle - needlefish -- v. 13. Newt - paradise fish -- v. 14. Paradoxical frog - poorwill -- v. 15. Porbeagle - rice rat -- v. 16. Rifleman - sea slug -- v. 17. Sea snake - sole -- v. 18. Solenodon - swan -- v. 19. Sweetfish - tree snake -- v. 20. Tree squirrel - water spider -- v. 21. Water vole - zorille -- v. 22. Index volume.
        ISBN 0-7614-7266-5 (set) -- ISBN 0-7614-7267-3 (v. 1) -- ISBN 0-7614-7268-1 (v. 2) -- ISBN 0-7614-7269-X (v. 3) -- ISBN 0-7614-7270-3 (v. 4) -- ISBN 0-7614-7271-1 (v. 5) -- ISBN 0-7614-7272-X (v. 6) -- ISBN 0-7614-7273-8 (v. 7) -- ISBN 0-7614-7274-6 (v. 8) -- ISBN 0-7614-7275-4 (v. 9) -- ISBN 0-7614-7276-2 (v. 10) -- ISBN 0-7614-7277-0 (v. 11) -- ISBN 0-7614-7278-9 (v. 12) -- ISBN 0-7614-7279-7 (v. 13) -- ISBN 0-7614-7280-0 (v. 14) -- ISBN 0-7614-7281-9 (v. 15) -- ISBN 0-7614-7282-7 (v. 16) -- ISBN 0-7614-7283-5 (v. 17) -- ISBN 0-7614-7284-3 (v. 18) -- ISBN 0-7614-7285-1 (v. 19) -- ISBN 0-7614-7286-X (v. 20) -- ISBN 0-7614-7287-8 (v. 21) -- ISBN 0-7614-7288-6 (v. 22)
    1. Zoology -- Dictionaries.   I. Burton, Robert, 1941-   . II. Title.

    QL9 .B796 2002
    590'.3--dc21
                                                                    2001017458

Printed in Malaysia
Bound in the United States of America

07 06 05 04 03 02 01   8 7 6 5 4 3 2 1

Brown Partworks
Project editor: Ben Hoare
Associate editors: Lesley Campbell-Wright, Rob Dimery, Robert Houston, Jane Lanigan, Sally McFall, Chris Marshall, Paul Thompson, Matthew D. S. Turner
Managing editor: Tim Cooke
Designer: Paul Griffin
Picture researchers: Brenda Clynch, Becky Cox
Illustrators: Ian Lycett, Catherine Ward
Indexer: Kay Ollerenshaw

Marshall Cavendish Corporation
Editorial director: Paul Bernabeo

Authors and Consultants

Dr. Roger Avery, BSc, PhD (University of Bristol)

Rob Cave, BA (University of Plymouth)

Fergus Collins, BA (University of Liverpool)

Dr. Julia J. Day, BSc (University of Bristol), PhD (University of London)

Tom Day, BA, MA (University of Cambridge), MSc (University of Southampton)

Bridget Giles, BA (University of London)

Leon Gray, BSc (University of London)

Tim Harris, BSc (University of Reading)

Richard Hoey, BSc, MPhil (University of Manchester), MSc (University of London)

Dr. Terry J. Holt, BSc, PhD (University of Liverpool)

Dr. Robert D. Houston, BA, MA (University of Oxford), PhD (University of Bristol)

Steve Hurley, BSc (University of London), MRes (University of York)

Tom Jackson, BSc (University of Bristol)

E. Vicky Jenkins, BSc (University of Edinburgh), MSc (University of Aberdeen)

Dr. Jamie McDonald, BSc (University of York), PhD (University of Birmingham)

Dr. Robbie A. McDonald, BSc (University of St. Andrews), PhD (University of Bristol)

Dr. James W. R. Martin, BSc (University of Leeds), PhD (University of Bristol)

Dr. Tabetha Newman, BSc, PhD (University of Bristol)

Dr. J. Pimenta, BSc (University of London), PhD (University of Bristol)

Dr. Kieren Pitts, BSc, MSc (University of Exeter), PhD (University of Bristol)

Dr. Stephen J. Rossiter, BSc (University of Sussex), PhD (University of Bristol)

Dr. Sugoto Roy, PhD (University of Bristol)

Dr. Adrian Seymour, BSc, PhD (University of Bristol)

Dr. Salma H. A. Shalla, BSc, MSc, PhD (Suez Canal University, Egypt)

Dr. S. Stefanni, PhD (University of Bristol)

Steve Swaby, BA (University of Exeter)

Matthew D. S. Turner, BA (University of Loughborough), FZSL (Fellow of the Zoological Society of London)

Alastair Ward, BSc (University of Glasgow), MRes (University of York)

Dr. Michael J. Weedon, BSc, MSc, PhD (University of Bristol)

Alwyne Wheeler, former Head of the Fish Section, Natural History Museum, London

Picture Credits
Ardea London: A. Greensmith 684, Peter Steyn 616; **Neil Bowman:** 583, 610, 674, 687, 713; **Bruce Coleman:** Erwin and Peggy Bauer 692, Mark N. Boulton 596, Dr. Hermann Brehm 646, Jane Burton 581, 638, 659, 700, Bob and Clara Calhoun 691, John Cancalosi 655, Mark Carwardine 698, Bruce Coleman Inc 665, 717, Alain Compost 677, 712, Gerald S. Cubitt 629, 630, M.P.L. Fogden 591, 600, 675, Jeff Foott 660, 689, 697, Christer Fredriksson 585, 662, Udo Hirsch 649, Charles and Sandra Hood 633, 639, 686, Janos Jurka 590, Tony Karacsonyi 632, Stephen J. Krassemann 656, Felix Labhardt 642, 709, 710, Gordon Langsbury 594, Wayne Lankinen 608, Werner Layer 598, Robert Maier 699, Luiz Claudio Marigo 624, 645, George McCarthy 714, Joe McDonald 611, Tero Niemi 618, 620, 627, Orion Press 584, Pacific Stock 640, William S. Paton 716, Mary Plage 650, Allan G. Potts 626, 680, Andrew Purcell 615, 631, 708, Marie Read 715, Hans Reinhard 701, Leonard Lee Rue 676, Jens Rydell 603, Dr. Frieder Sauer 580, John Shaw 661, Alan Stillwell 588, Alan Taylor 589, Kim Taylor 599, 641, 643, 644, 711, Uwe Walz 587, Jorg & Petra Wegner 586, 658, Staffan Widstrand 625, Wild-Type Productions 592, Rod Williams 595, 605, 657, 671, Konrad Wothe 681, 704, J.P. Zwaenepoel 690; **Corbis:** Brandon D. Cole 604, 635, Pam Gardner/Frank Lane Picture Agency 621, Eric and David Hosking 619, 678, Joe McDonald 617, Fritz Polking/Frank Lane Picture Agency 606, Kevin Schafer 648, Michael S. Yamashita 679; **Chris Gomersall:** 593, 612, 628, 705; **NHPA:** Jim Bain 652, Stephen Dalton 633, 637, 682, 683, K. Ghani 672, John Hartley 667, Daniel Heuclin 663, 666, B. Jones & M. Shimlock 669, Gerald Lacz 597, Michael Leach 607, Trevor McDonald 688, Michael Morcome 582, Roger Tidman 609, Roy Waller 634, 707, Dave Watts 702, 703, Norbert Wu 654, 668; **NOAA Photo Library:** 695, National Marine Fisheries Service 696; **Planet Earth Pictures:** 601, Pete Atkinson 694, Peter David 653, J. Downer 614, Doug Perrine 693; **Still Pictures:** Paul Glendell 651, F. Graner 706, Hubert/Klein 664, Yves Lefevre 670; **Andy Swash:** 613, 623. **Artwork:** Catherine Ward 673.

Contents

CRAB SPIDER

Crab spiders have superb camouflage. They can assume the coloration of flowers, leaves, tree bark and even bird droppings.

CRAB SPIDERS ARE SO CALLED because of their flattish body and of the way they scuttle rapidly sideways, in the manner of the true crabs. Their four pairs of legs are long and curved, the first two or three pairs being shorter than the rest. The legs are usually held out from the sides of the body. Most crab spiders are less than ½ inch (1.3 cm) long, though the giant crab spiders may grow to 1 inch (2.5 cm). There are 3,000 to 5,000 species of crab spider worldwide, distributed between the families Thomisidae, Sparassidae and Selenopidae.

Beauty lies hidden

Crab spiders' colors and markings blend in with their surroundings. This helps them to camouflage themselves from predators and also aids them in capturing their prey. Many crab spiders inhabit leaf litter or low-growing vegetation. Some position themselves along the stems and leaves of plants, head downward, with the legs on each side held together in the same plane as the piece of foliage. Others spend most of their time in flowers. Crab spiders may remain for several days, or even weeks, in the same position. *Thomisus onustus* is often a bright pink color, blending perfectly with the flowers of the bell heath and of certain orchids. Another species, *Misumena vatia*, sometimes called the white death, mainly occurs in white or yellow plants, the white varieties being found in flowers such as the butterfly orchid, and the yellow varieties in mullein and gorse. Like *T. onustus*, this species can alter its color to white, yellow or green in order to match its surroundings. It may take the crab spider 2–3 days to effect a color change.

Danger in a flower

Crab spiders take a wide variety of small insects and other invertebrates. Rather than making a web, a crab spider lies in wait and pounces on its prey when it is within range. The crab spider seizes its prey and bites it, pumping a poison into the victim's body. The venom is held in a saclike poison gland that is covered with secretory cells. Muscle fibers encircle the gland. When the fibers are contracted, venom is forced down a long duct running through the chelicerae (fangs) and into the victim. The venom paralyzes the prey, though it is not dangerous to humans. The victim is drained of its body fluids through cuts made by the crab spider's jaws and the lifeless body is discarded.

Those crab spiders that inhabit flower heads often take insects such as hoverflies, bees and butterflies, which visit the flowers for nectar. Sometimes the prey is bitten in a nonfatal area, such as the abdomen. When this is the case, the crab spider manipulates the prey until it is able to administer a fatal bite to the head or thorax, where the central nervous system can be more directly reached. If the crab spider captures large numbers of prey it may hang the surplus below its hiding place for future consumption.

Tentative courtship

As with other spider species, crab spiders grow by shedding their skins at regular intervals. A few days before the male crab spider undergoes his final molt he builds a small band or web on which to discharge a drop of seminal fluid. This he takes up into each of his two palps (sensory appendages situated near the mouth) before going in search of a mate. There is little preliminary courtship between crab spiders.

CRAB SPIDERS

PHYLUM	**Arthropoda**
CLASS	**Arachnida**
ORDER	**Araneae**
FAMILY	**Thomisidae, Sparassidae and Selenopidae**

GENUS AND SPECIES **3,000 to 5,000 species, including *Thomisus onustus*; *Misumena vatia*; and *Xysticus cristatus***

LENGTH
Varies according to species. Head and body: up to 1¼ in. (3 cm) in *Isopoda*; most species less than ½ in. (1.3 cm).

DISTINCTIVE FEATURES
Flattened body; 4 pairs of long, curved legs; in many species coloration matches environment

DIET
Invertebrates, especially insects such as bees, hoverflies and butterflies

BREEDING
Varies according to species. Breeding season: spring and summer; number of eggs: 30 to 50 (*X. cristatus*).

LIFE SPAN
Up to 1 year

HABITAT
Grasslands, light woodland, hedgerows and marshes, usually on flowers and other low-growing plants and in leaf litter

DISTRIBUTION
Virtually worldwide

STATUS
Many species common

Misumena vatia can adopt green, yellow or white coloration. Camouflaged against the petals of a flower such as an oxeye daisy (above), this crab spider quickly strikes prey that comes within range.

Tentative caressings with the legs enable the two partners to recognize each other and stimulate the female to accept the male. Grasping the female by a leg, the male inserts the sperm package into her genital aperture. If she has already mated, she does not allow the male to approach but menaces him by raising her front legs and jerking her body. If he persists, she may seize and kill him. Mating may last for less than a minute or continue for several hours.

In one species, *Xysticus cristatus*, the male employs a device to prevent the female from seizing him. He binds her legs to the ground with threads of silk, after encouraging her to accept his initial advances by caressing her. The silken structure that results is known as a bridal veil. When mating is complete, the female is delayed just long enough in freeing herself from her bonds to allow the male to escape.

Most crab spiders lay their eggs in early summer. The female makes a silken saucer in which to lay her eggs. She then covers this construction with another silken layer, forming an egg-sac. This may be built between leaves lying on the ground or among foliage. Sometimes the female makes a silken tent within which she sits, guarding the eggs. Many females eat nothing during the period of incubation and become extremely emaciated. Others capture prey as usual, although they never stray far from their eggs. Young crab spiders are hatched as miniatures of their parents, although they often differ considerably to the adults in color.

Prey for many

Crab spiders have many predators. Small mammals, birds, reptiles and amphibians all eat them, as do some beetles, ants and centipedes. Certain species of wasps and ichneumon flies lay their eggs inside the body tissues of living crab spiders. Not least, considerable crab spider mortality is caused by different species of crab spiders killing and eating one another.

CRAKE

Baillon's crake is rarely seen by humans. Crakes are usually highly elusive and frequent thick cover in wet habitats such as marshes and swamps.

CRAKES ARE MEMBERS OF the rail family and in North America are known as rails. They are small to medium-sized birds, which grow to 8–25½ inches (20–65 cm) in length. Crakes have moderately long legs and toes and short, rounded wings. Their plumage varies from buff or chestnut to greenish blue or nearly black. Crakes are distinguished from other members of the family Rallidae by a short, conical bill.

The spotted crake, *Porzana porzana*, has olive-brown upperparts streaked with white and a gray, white-speckled breast. The bill is yellow with a red base. Baillon's crake (*P. pusilla*), the little crake (*P. parva*) and the sora (*P. carolina*) are very like the spotted crake in plumage, but the first two are much smaller, being about the size of the starling, *Sturnus vulgaris*. The sora is distinguishable by its strongly barred underparts and by the black patch on its throat and face. The ruddy crake, *Laterallus ruber*, is intermediate in size, with a dark brown back, reddish brown breast and white chin.

Crakes are represented worldwide. They are found in Madagascar, Australia, the Philippines and many other Pacific islands, as well as on the main landmasses. The spotted, Baillon's and little crakes are European species that also range across parts of central Asia. Baillon's crake is also found in southern Africa, Australia and New Zealand, an unusual discontinuous distribution with isolated populations in different parts of the world. The sora is a widespread breeding species in North America, ranging to central South America during the winter.

Elusive birds

Like their near relative the corncrake, *Crex crex*, crakes are skulking birds. They live in thick cover and fly only short distances, except when migrating. Their impressive capacity for sustained flying is demonstrated by the sora's transatlantic flights: at least 14 soras have been recorded in the British Isles. The spotted crake has made trips in the opposite direction, turning up in Greenland and the Caribbean.

There is a gradation of habitat preference among the members of the rail family (Rallidae). The corncrake prefers grasslands and the coots require open sheets of water where they can freely dive. The crakes prefer intermediate conditions, in the marshy banks of rivers and lakes and in dense reedbeds where there is a sodden mat of vegetation. The sora fills the same environmental niche in North America as the spotted crake in Europe; both species keep to the drier borders of wetlands. Baillon's and little crakes prefer the flooded areas in the middle of the swamps, and the little crake in particular frequents marshes with open pools.

Crakes feed on the aquatic animals and plants that they find living at the surface of the swamp water and in the muddy areas between the pools. Their main prey is water snails and insects such as water beetles, mayflies and mosquitoes, as well as their larvae. Crakes feed on a variety of water plants and grasses. In North America, soras eat mainly seeds during the fall, including those of wild rice.

Well concealed nests

Crakes build their nests in swamps and marshes, on either tussocks of grass or small islands. The sora and Baillon's crake sometimes build basket-like nests in clumps of sedge and other marsh plants, 1 foot (30 cm) or more above the surface of the water. The stems of the plants around the nest are interwoven to form a canopy that hides the nest from possible enemies. The nest itself is made of dead rushes and grasses and is lined with finer vegetation. The sora sometimes also constructs a runway of nesting material, leading to the nest.

Crakes generally lay 6 to 12 eggs, though the spotted crake has been known to lay up to 15. Both parents brood the eggs in turn for up to

SORA

CLASS	**Aves**
ORDER	**Gruiformes**
FAMILY	**Rallidae**
GENUS AND SPECIES	***Porzana carolina***

ALTERNATIVE NAMES
Sora rail; Carolina crake

WEIGHT
About 2–2¼ oz. (60–62 g)

LENGTH
**Head to tail: 8¾ in. (22 cm);
wingspan: 12–14¼ in. (30–36 cm)**

DISTINCTIVE FEATURES
**Short, conical, yellow bill; moderately long
legs and toes; black patch on face and throat
(adult only); strongly barred underparts;
white undertail**

DIET
**Aquatic invertebrates such as water snails,
water beetles, mayflies and mosquitoes; seeds**

BREEDING
**Age at first breeding: 1 year; breeding
season: April–July; number of eggs: usually
10 to 12; incubation period: 18–20 days;
fledging period: 19–20 days; breeding
interval: 1 year**

LIFE SPAN
Not known

HABITAT
**Freshwater and brackish marshes, wet
meadows, fields of rice and grain; also salt
marshes (migration only)**

DISTRIBUTION
**Central Canada south to central Peru; also
on some Caribbean islands**

STATUS
Locally common

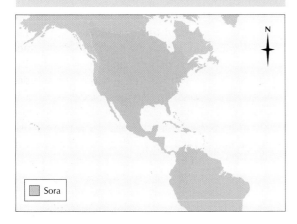
Sora

3 weeks. Incubation commences before all the eggs are laid, so the chicks emerge at variable intervals over a period of several days. The young birds are able to leave the nest shortly after hatching and the male cares for them while the female incubates the remaining eggs. After all the eggs are hatched, both parents guard the chicks, feeding them until they are 1 week old. Sometimes the chicks divide into two parties, each under the charge of one parent.

Which crake is which?

Crakes are secretive birds that are difficult to identify. Their preference for living in marshes with thick vegetation, water and mud, which are also home to swarms of mosquitoes, makes them very difficult to observe. The description of their habits given above is only a general outline. As crakes are infrequently sighted, detailed information is not available for many species.

The difficulty of identification and study is clearly illustrated by the experience of a highly competent ornithologist who embarked on a study of Baillon's crakes. Years after he carried out his in-depth research, the birds he had been watching were identified from his photographs as young little crakes. In the 1950s and 1960s Baillon's crakes were identified in various parts of Europe by comparing their calls with a recording made in 1948. However, in 1968 a crake making a call that sounded very similar to this recording was trapped and found to be a female little crake.

Like most crakes, the little crake eats aquatic invertebrates, seeds and shoots. It feeds while swimming or running along plant stems.

CRANE

In Hokkaido, northern Japan, red-crowned cranes are resident all year, but a second population flies from eastern Russia to Korea for the winter. Young cranes learn the migration routes of their species by accompanying their parents south to the wintering grounds.

A LONG-LEGGED, LONG-NECKED, heronlike bird, the largest crane stands up to 5 feet (1.5 m) high, with a wingspan of 8¼ feet (2.5 m). There are 15 species of these striking birds, most of them now rare. Cranes are very wary, and disturbance of their habitat has caused their declines as much as hunting. However, ornithologists believe that in historical times some crane species have never been numerous.

The various species of crane are often distinguished by the patches of color around the head and neck. The common, or Eurasian, crane, *Grus grus*, has a red crown with black and white on the head and neck. The whooping crane (*G. americana*), sandhill crane (*G. canadensis*), sarus crane (*G. antigone*) and brolga (*G. rubicunda*) all have red patches on the head. The black-crowned crane, *Balearica paronina*, is often said to be the most striking species. It has white ovals behind the eyes, a red wattle and a plume of orange-brown feathers that is a little like the crest on a Roman helmet. The red-crowned, or Japanese, crane, *G. japonensis*, is very distinctive, with its starkly contrasting black-and-white plumage. The head and neck are black except for a white patch on the crown reaching to the eyes. The body is pure white except for the black secondary feathers, which form a black rear border to the wings when spread.

Call like a trombone

An unusual feature of cranes' internal anatomy is the windpipe, which may reach 5 feet (1.5 m) in length, half of which is coiled within the breastbone. The remarkably long windpipe gives the cranes their loud, trombonelike calls, which may carry for 1 mile (1.6 km) or more.

Cranes eat mainly vegetation, including leaves, roots, seeds and fruits. Sometimes they attack crops, a habit for which they are persecuted. On balance, however, cranes probably help farmers, by eating a variety of harmful insects. They thrust their long bills into the soil to take wireworms and other insect larvae. Cranes also occasionally prey on small vertebrates, including frogs, reptiles, birds and mammals.

COMMON CRANE

CLASS	**Aves**
ORDER	**Gruiformes**
FAMILY	**Gruidae**
GENUS AND SPECIES	***Grus grus***

ALTERNATIVE NAME
Eurasian crane

LENGTH
**Head to tail: 3⅔–4 ft. (1.1–1.2 m);
wingspan: 7¼–8¼ ft. (2.2–2.5 m)**

DISTINCTIVE FEATURES
**Very large; long neck; long, strong legs;
powerful, daggerlike bill; plumage mainly
gray with red crown, black neck and white
patch running from behind eye down neck;
cloak of loose feathers over tail**

DIET
**Mainly roots, leaves, fruits, seeds and
invertebrates; sometimes small vertebrates**

BREEDING
**Age at first breeding: 4–6 years; breeding
season: April–August; number of eggs: 2;
incubation period: 30 days; fledging period:
65–70 days; breeding interval: 1 year**

LIFE SPAN
Probably up to 30–40 years

HABITAT
**Breeds in reedy wetlands and swampy
clearings in coniferous forests and (far north
only) on treeless moors; winters in open
country, especially cultivated land**

DISTRIBUTION
**Breeds from Norway east through Russia to
eastern Siberia, and south as far as Central
Asia and Mongolia; winters in parts of the
Mediterranean, northwestern Africa, Sudan,
Ethiopia, Middle East and southern Asia**

STATUS
Uncommon; population: about 250,000

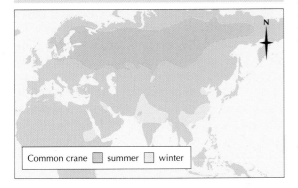

Common crane ▨ summer ▢ winter

A family in decline

Crane populations are becoming reduced in many parts of the world. The Siberian crane, *G. leucogeranus*, and the whooping crane are both classed as endangered and another five species are vulnerable. Cranes breed in secluded wetlands, which are steadily being cleared for agricultural use. The birds are also shot for sport, or because of the danger they are believed to pose to crops.

The future of the whooping crane now seems relatively secure, but 50 years ago the species appeared to be heading for extinction, having

been reduced to about 20 birds. Determined conservation measures have enabled the population of whooping cranes to climb slowly to more than 150. This figure is well below the numbers that existed when Europeans first arrived in North America and hunting began, but it does offer the prospect of more a stable population in the future. The whooping crane breeds only in Wood Buffalo National Park in Alberta, Canada, and like other cranes it has only a slow rate of reproduction. In the fall the population migrates south to the Gulf Coast of Texas.

The red-crowned crane is the third-rarest crane species in the world. It is classified as vulnerable and today numbers only 1,700 to 2,000 birds in its breeding grounds in Hokkaido, northern Japan, China and southeastern Russia.

Paired cranes engage in periods of intense dancing prior to mating. Ornithologists believe that one purpose of the crane dance is to develop bonds between mates.

Crane chicks can run almost from hatching but remain with their parents until the start of the next breeding season. The main breeding grounds of the common crane (above) are in Siberia.

The sandhill crane of North America is less threatened. In places this species is actually increasing its numbers.

Distribution

Apart from the sandhill and whooping cranes of North America, the cranes mainly live in Asia. The common crane occurs in Europe and Asia, breeding mainly in northern areas. In medieval times this species was quite common in the British Isles, where it bred until about 1600. Apart from a tiny population in southeastern England, the common crane is now seen only rarely in Britain. Flocks sometimes appear in the south of the country, having been driven across the North Sea by bad weather.

Most cranes form flocks and are migratory, moving from summer to winter quarters. The birds fly in a V-shape, or an echelon formation. They fly with slow, measured wingbeats, and with necks outstretched. When on migration they are believed to reach altitudes of up to 10,500 feet (3,200 m).

Dancing cranes

Throughout the year, but particularly in the breeding season, cranes indulge in a spectacular ritual dance. They walk around each other with quick, stiff-legged steps and wings half spread, occasionally bowing and stretching. The tempo of the dance increases, and they leap into the air, flying up to a height of 15 feet (4.5 m) or more and drifting slowly down. This dance is not confined to pairs of cranes, for sometimes whole flocks including juveniles will join together to dance. During the dance some of the cranes pick sticks or leaves with their bills, throw them into the air and stab at them as they fall.

Cranes make their nests on the ground, piling up a heap of vegetation. The site is usually on open, marshy ground, or sometimes in a few inches of standing water. On dry ground the nest may be little more than a patch of flattened vegetation. The usual clutch size is two eggs, the second being laid 2 days after the first. Incubation starts as soon as the first egg is laid, which therefore hatches 2 days before the second. The chick can run almost from hatching and, in the care of the male, leaves the nest, while the female continues to incubate the second egg. Later, when both chicks have left the nest, each may be taken care of by one parent. The young cranes' legs grow very rapidly and in 1 month are full grown. By the same time the birds' wings have hardly developed: the young do not fly until 9 10 weeks after hatching.

In Japan cranes are symbols of longevity and in folklore they were reputed to live for up to 1,000 years. Even in real life cranes are known to live for at least 50 years.

Influence on human culture

The dancing of cranes is one of the most spectacular performances in the bird world. Other birds may have a more colorful and elaborate plumage to set off their displays, but the cranes' size, combined with the energy of their dances, makes them a particularly impressive sight to humans. A dancing flock of cranes is especially spectacular. The brolga of Australia, also popularly known as the native companion, dances in troops lined up in rows of 20 to 30. The dance of the brolga is the basis for some of the dances at aboriginal *corroborees* (traditional gatherings). There are also crane dances in other parts of the world, where the cranes symbolize the returning spring. The aboriginal Ainu tribesmen of Japan have a dance that commemorates the *Tanchō* or red-crowned crane.

Cranes have a symbolic importance in some oriental martial arts, such as *wing-chun kung fu* in China and *Goju-ryu* karate in Okinawa, Japan. The choice of the crane as a symbol originates from the birds' hunting strategies: they often use their legs to pin down prey with a stamping motion, a style copied by practitioners of some martial arts.

The red-crowned crane often appears in Japanese art and literature and for hundreds of years the species was protected by the Japanese veneration for it as a symbol of eternal life. However, in the 19th century red-crowned cranes were exterminated everywhere in Japan except for in the Kushiro swamp, Hokkaido. The species' last stronghold was inaccessible to humans, and the Kushiro cranes did not migrate to areas where they would be more vulnerable. Numbers dropped to 20 in 1924, but strict preservation has since enabled the species to recover. There are now more than 600 red-crowned cranes. They visit nearby farms in winter, where they are fed grain and rice by farmers.

The sandhill crane is one of two species native to North America. It breeds in northwestern Canada and migrates south to Texas, Cuba and Mexico for the winter.

CRANE FLY

In common with other true flies, crane flies have only two wings. The drumstick-shaped halteres, situated directly behind the wings, help the crane fly to maintain a level flight course.

CRANE FLIES ARE THIN-BODIED INSECTS with long, threadlike legs and are found in great numbers during much of the summer. They are related to midges, mosquitoes and gnats and, like these insects, crane flies have very delicate wings and legs. The male is readily recognized because the end of his abdomen is widened and clubbed, whereas that of the the female is drawn out to form a pointed ovipositor (egg-laying organ).

Crane flies are often referred to as daddy longlegs in Britain. In the United States the name daddy longlegs is applied to harvestmen or harvesters, which are relatives of the true spiders. Both crane flies and harvestmen have long, fragile legs, but there the similarity ends. Crane flies belong to the family Tipulidae, the largest family in the order Diptera (flies), with about 1,500 species in North America and 12,000 species worldwide. They are true flies and have complex eyes and only two wings, rather than the four wings found in most insects. Crane flies usually occur near water sources or near high concentrations of plants.

Crane fly larvae are long, soft, fat grubs without legs. They feed on roots, including those of grasses, which is why they can ruin a lawn so easily and thus become unpopular with humans.

Larvae strip grasslands bare

Adult crane flies are generally short-lived and do not feed very often. Their mouthparts are modified into a snoutlike proboscis with which they suck up water and flower nectar. Most of the feeding is done by the larvae, which are grayish and vary from just a few millimeters to over 1½ inches (3.8 cm) in length. The larvae begin to feed immediately after hatching, using their very strong jaws to eat the roots and lower stems of plants. Most crane fly larvae feed on grasses, but the larvae of some larger species also feed on cultivated plants such as marigolds, oats and potatoes. The larvae of these larger crane fly species are commonly known as leatherjackets.

The effect of a heavy infestation of leatherjackets on grassland may be to produce extensive bare brown patches. Gardeners and groundsmen sometimes combat leatherjackets by placing large groundsheets over lawns. The larvae often venture above ground at night to feed on grass stems, so covering the ground by day induces the larvae to rise to the surface as if it were night. After a while the covering is removed and the larvae may be swept up by the thousands.

Some aquatic crane fly larvae are predatory. They feed on small worms, dragonfly larvae and the larvae of any other insect species that are readily available.

CRANE FLIES

PHYLUM	**Arthropoda**
CLASS	**Insecta**
ORDER	**Diptera**
FAMILY	**Tipulidae**

GENUS AND SPECIES   **About 12,000 species, including 1,500 in North America**

ALTERNATIVE NAMES
Mosquito hawk; bobbing gnat; leatherjacket (larvae of larger species only); daddy longlegs (Britain only)

LENGTH
Adult wingspan: ⅔–2⅔ in. (1.5–6.5 cm)

DISTINCTIVE FEATURES
Adult: slender, elongated body and legs; delicate, long, narrow wings, folded over body at rest. Larva: long, soft, fat body.

DIET
Adult: flower nectar, honeydew and other liquids; most adults rarely feed. Larva: decomposing plant matter (small species); plant roots and stems (larger species); some aquatic species predatory.

BREEDING
Breeding season: usually spring and summer; number of eggs: up to about 100; larval period: usually less than 1 year

LIFE SPAN
Adult: several days

HABITAT
Variety of damp habitats with lush vegetation. Adult: mainly in shaded woodland. Larva: many species aquatic; others in soil, decaying wood and leaf litter.

DISTRIBUTION
Worldwide, except in coldest regions

STATUS
Some species superabundant; others common

Although the adults and larvae of some crane fly species are regarded as pests, the Tipulidae are an important food source for other species. Fish, amphibians, invertebrates and at least 90 species of birds in New York State alone are known to eat tipulids. Moreover, in many freshwater habitats, especially ponds, streams and damp floodplains, tipulid larvae play an important role in shredding riparian (bankside) leaf litter. By doing so the larvae make plant matter available to other species that are capable of feeding on only small organic particles.

Breed in damp places

The most common British species of crane fly is the large, grayish-bodied *Tipula oleracea*, which is particularly abundant in late summer. It often flies low over the ground with its long legs trailing. The males of some of the smaller species swarm in nuptial flights before mating. Eggs are laid in water, damp earth, moss or saturated wood, and the larvae and pupae are aquatic or semiaquatic. Those species that are most troublesome to humans and live on land also require moisture. Periods of drought often kill off the larvae of these species in large numbers.

Most crane fly species breed in the summer, the females laying eggs from June onward. In other species, breeding is more or less continuous throughout the year. Female crane flies that lay their eggs in spring or early summer, having themselves emerged from overwintering pupae,

Crane flies are vulnerable due to the fragile nature of their legs and wings. The legs trail behind the body in flight and are easily entangled in spiders' webs.

In most species of crane fly the adults rarely feed and the larvae feed only on decaying vegetation. It is the larvae of the larger crane flies that can be serious pests on farms and in gardens.

may give rise to a further generation in a matter of weeks. On emerging from its pupa, the male immediately seeks a mate. Often the males emerge some time before the females and this may mean a protracted period of searching for a partner. Occasionally a male will wait as a female emerges from her pupal case and mate with her while her skin is still soft and damp.

The female lays her tiny, black, seedlike eggs by thrusting her ovipositor deep into the soil. From about June onward she may lay up to 100 eggs, which hatch in about 2 weeks. The small larvae, with wrinkled and flexible skins, are very tough. The larvae of the larger crane fly species feed and increase in size by shedding their skin to form the familiar leatherjackets. Finally they change to pupae. As the time for emergence approaches, these wriggle toward the surface of the ground, helped by downward-pointing bristles on the body, and thrust themselves part way out. Then the pupal skin splits behind the head and along the lines of the wings, and the adult fly forces its way out.

Aquatic crane fly larvae have five pairs of false legs, lost when the insects become adults, which enable them to crawl about the bottoms of ponds and streams. They breathe by taking oxygen dissolved in the water or by rising to the surface at intervals to take in air. The pupae remain active and have two hornlike processes on the head, with which to take in air from above the surface of the water.

Gyroscopic flight control

Like all true flies, a crane fly has only one pair of wings, the second, rear pair being reduced to two club-shaped rods called halteres. The halteres are difficult to see in small flies such as blowflies and houseflies, but are easily visible to the naked human eye in crane flies. *Halteres* was the name given to the two weights or bags of sand that Ancient Greek athletes held in each hand to help throw themselves forward in the long jump. The name is appropriate to the vestigial (imperfectly developed) wings of true flies because they provide balance in flight.

While a crane fly is in the air, its halteres are rapidly vibrated in the same figure-of-eight motion as the wings, though out of phase with them. In doing so they act in the same way as the gyroscopes that are the basis of an automatic pilot. Rotating at great speed, a gyroscope in an airplane stays level while the fuselage rolls, yaws and pitches about it. Instruments attached to the gyroscope measure the degree of movement and automatically inform the controls of the steps needed to bring the airplane back on course. Halteres function in much the same way. At the base of each haltere are sense organs that detect strains and stresses as the fly changes course. If a crane fly changes direction suddenly, perhaps due to a gust of wind, the stems of its halteres are twisted. The sensors in the haltere stems send information to the fly's brain and the fly adjusts its flight accordingly to maintain a level course.

CRAYFISH

THE CRAYFISH ARE FRESHWATER crustaceans some 4–19½ inches (10–50 cm) in length. Most are colored sandy yellow, green or dark brown. The head and thorax are covered with a single shell, or carapace, which ends in front in a sharp-pointed rostrum. The eyes are compound and stalked. On the head are a pair of small antennules, which are well supplied with sense organs, and a pair of long antennae. The latter are organs of touch, with excretory organs at the base. Crayfish have strong jaws and two pairs of smaller accessory jaws, or maxillae. The second pair of maxillae drives water across 20 pairs of feathery gills.

On the thorax there are three pairs of appendages, which pass food to the jaws, a pair of stout pincers and four pairs of legs, which crayfish use to walk forward. The abdomen is segmented and has five pairs of limbs on its underside. The first pair are grooved in the male and are used to introduce sperm onto the female. The other four are swimmerets, small appendages that aid locomotion. A crayfish can escape predators by swimming speedily backward with forward flicks of its abdomen, which ends in a fan-shaped tail.

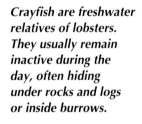

Crayfish are freshwater relatives of lobsters. They usually remain inactive during the day, often hiding under rocks and logs or inside burrows.

Emerge at night

The two families of crayfish are confined almost entirely to temperate regions: the Astacidae in the Northern Hemisphere, the Parastacidae in the Southern Hemisphere. There are no crayfish in Africa, but several species are present in Madagascar. Crayfish are also absent from the greater part of Asia, although they do occur in Korea and in the northern islands of Japan.

Crayfish generally live in rivers, streams and lakes. They are nocturnal and feed on a variety of vegetable and animal matter, including insect larvae, snails, worms, tadpoles and organic detritus. During the day crayfish remain within burrows or under stones and logs. The largest crayfish, *Astacopsis gouldi*, inhabits streams and rivers in northern Tasmania and may weigh up to 9 pounds (4 kg). It is the largest freshwater invertebrate in the world. Another of the Tasmanian crayfish, sometimes known as the land crab, habitually leaves standing fresh water and burrows in damp earth in forests. In Mammoth Cave in Kentucky, there are several crayfish living in the underground waters. These cave-dwelling species are colorless and blind. Their eyes have gone, leaving only the stalks.

The hard shell of a crayfish (Astacus pallipes, above) gives protection but limits the animal's growth. As a result the crayfish must regularly shed its shell and grow a new, larger one.

CRAYFISH

PHYLUM	**Arthropoda**
CLASS	**Crustacea**
ORDER	**Decapoda**
FAMILY	**Astacidae (Northern Hemisphere); Parastacidae (Southern Hemisphere)**

GENUS AND SPECIES   **Many species, including signal crayfish, *Pacifastacus leniusculus*; noble crayfish, *Astacus astacus*; Tasmanian giant crayfish, *Astacopsis gouldi*; and white-clawed crayfish, *Austropotamobius pallipes***

ALTERNATIVE NAMES
Crawfish; crawdad; yabbie (Australia only)

LENGTH
4–19½ in. (10–50 cm)

DIET
Wide range of small aquatic animals and plant matter, including detritus

DISTINCTIVE FEATURES
Resemble small lobsters; hard carapace (shell) covering head and thorax; 2 pairs of long antennae; 1 pair of large pincers; 4 pairs of limbs on thorax and 5 pairs on abdomen; abdomen ends in fan-shaped tail

BREEDING
***Austropotamobius pallipes*. Age at first breeding: 3–4 years; breeding season: usually fall; number of eggs: up to 100; breeding interval: 1 year.**

LIFE SPAN
Up to 15 years

HABITAT
Streams, rivers, canals, lakes, reservoirs and water-filled quarries

DISTRIBUTION
Temperate regions of Americas, Eurasia, Southeast Asia and Australasia, also Japan and Madagascar; absent from Africa

STATUS
Some species relatively common; growing number of species under threat

No larval stage

Crayfish mate in the fall. The male turns the female over and sheds milt through the first pair of abdominal appendages onto her abdomen, where it sticks. The female then enters a burrow to lay her eggs, which may number more than 200, depending on the species. These become attached to bristles on her swimmerets, where they are fertilized by contact with the milt.

The fertilized eggs hatch the following spring. Unusually for crustaceans, crayfish have no larval stage. The newly hatched crayfish are transparent and are tiny replicas of the adults. They grasp the female's swimmerets with their claws and remain attached for some time.

Periodic molts

In common with most crustaceans and insects, crayfish grow by periodic molts. During the process of molting calcium salts—the chalky matter in the old shell—are taken back into the blood, ready to be laid down again in the new shell being formed beneath the old one. The old shell, by now merely a tough cuticle, is shed and the body takes up water and swells. The calcium salts are then laid down in the new cuticle, which gradually hardens.

Molting takes 6 hours, during which time the crayfish fasts and stays in hiding. Many crayfish die during this vulnerable period due both to an increased risk of predation and to the many attendant difficulties of the process itself.

Crayfish plague

Crayfish plague is a disease caused by the fungus *Aphanomyces astaci*, and only affects freshwater crayfish. All native European crayfish species are highly susceptible to the disease. Individuals affected by the plague may show abnormal behavior, such as daylight activity and walking on tiptoe and in more severe cases individuals may be seen struggling on their backs or leaving the water. It is thought that the disease was introduced into Italy in the 1860s and spread rapidly across much of Europe. It devastated indigenous crayfish populations, particularly those of the noble crayfish, *Astacus astacus*.

CRESTED LARK

THE CRESTED LARK IS slightly larger than the house sparrow, *Passer domesticus*, measuring about 6¾ inches (17 cm) from head to tail. Several other larks have crests, but these are not as conspicuous as those of the crested lark and the very similar thekla lark, *Galerida theklae*. Some ornithologists formerly placed these two larks in the same species. The thekla lark is smaller, with shorter, narrower wings, and it has a distinctly shorter and less pointed bill than the crested lark. The two birds also have different songs.

The breeding range of the crested lark extends from the Atlantic coasts of France and Spain east to northeastern China. It includes northern India, Arabia, North Africa, the fringes of the Sahara Desert and the Red Sea coast south to Ethiopia and Somalia. In historic times the crested lark spread up through Europe from the Mediterranean and in 1850–1900 it colonized parts of Scandinavia. This northward expansion was short-lived, however, and the crested lark had vanished as a breeding species from Norway and Sweden by 1989. The thekla lark is found only in Portugal, Spain, northwest Africa and parts of East Africa.

Bird of arid lands

The crested lark usually lives on flat, rather barren country. It inhabits steppes and the fringes of deserts where there are patches of warm, sandy soil with coarse grass and low, thorny bushes. The species is also common along roadsides, in gardens and on wasteland and garbage tips in towns. As the steppes of central Europe became cultivated, the crested lark's range spread as suitable habitats were formed along roads and railways. The crested lark is also present in the Atlas Mountains of Morocco.

Where the ranges of the crested and thekla larks overlap, the two species generally breed in different habitats. The thekla lark requires a mixture of habitats, such as open, sandy areas with a scattering of rocks or dry streambeds flanked by bushes.

The crested lark lives mainly on grain, from oats and wheat and the seeds of grasses and weeds. It also picks the undigested grains out of horse droppings. Experts believe that in this way horse dung constitutes major food source for the crested lark. It is thought that the species' decline in western and central Europe is linked to the postwar decline in the numbers of horses. In the breeding season, the crested lark catches beetles, grasshoppers and insect larvae for its chicks.

The crested lark's song, a liquid whistle of three or four syllables, is like that of the skylark, *Alauda cristata*, but is not as loud or continuous. The crested lark sings from high in the air, perhaps 100–200 feet (30–60 m) up. It does not sing while ascending or descending and is not as conspicuous as the skylark, which rises slowly, singing all the time. The crested lark also sings while perched on suitable buildings, trees and telephone wires.

Shelters its eggs from the sun

The well hidden nest is built by both sexes from grass stems that are woven into a cup and lined with rootlets or hair. It is set under low bushes or in thick grass, or on the roofs of sheds or houses. Sometimes a dome is woven over the nest cup. The female incubates the eggs alone. In hot weather she does not sit on the eggs, but stands over them, sheltering them from the sun's heat. The eggs hatch in 11–13 days. After the chicks have emerged, the female eats the eggshells or drops them 1–2 feet (30–60 cm) from the nest. The chicks stay in the nest for a week or more, but cannot fly for at least another week.

The crested lark is a ground-dwelling bird of flat, dry country in Europe, Africa and Asia. Its rather plain, sandy coloration provides excellent camouflage.

Crested larks usually raise their crests when they are looking for a mate or are alarmed by a nearby predator.

CRESTED LARK

CLASS	**Aves**
ORDER	**Passeriformes**
FAMILY	**Alaudidae**
GENUS AND SPECIES	***Galerida cristata***

LENGTH
**Head to tail: about 6¾ in. (17 cm);
wingspan: 11½–15 in. (29–38 cm)**

DISTINCTIVE FEATURES
**Long, spiky crest; heavily streaked,
pale brown plumage**

DIET
Seeds and invertebrates

BREEDING
**Age at first breeding: 1 year; breeding
season: March–July; number of eggs: usually
3 to 5; incubation period: 11–13 days;
fledging period: 15–16 days; breeding
interval: 2 or 3 broods per year**

LIFE SPAN
Probably up to 10 years

HABITAT
**Open and lightly wooded country, including
non-intensively cultivated land, grassland,
steppe, semidesert and urban wasteland**

DISTRIBUTION
**Much of Europe east through Central and
southern Asia to India and China, and south
to tropical Africa and Arabia**

STATUS
**Generally common; abundant in some areas
but declining in western and central Europe**

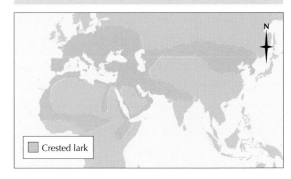

Crested lark

Camouflaged larks

As a ground-nesting bird, the crested lark is preyed upon by snakes and foxes as well as by birds of prey such as hawks and kestrels. Camouflage provides the crested lark with an important means of defense against such predators. With the obvious exception of the male black lark, *Melanocorypha yeltoniensis*, of Russia and Central Asia, larks generally have a brown plumage, streaked with gray or buff. When perched or feeding on the ground, or sitting on the nest, they are very hard to see. Larks that live in the sparsely vegetated margins of deserts, such as those of the genera *Ammomanes*, *Mirafra* and *Spizocorys*, blend in particularly well with their environment. A comparison of their plumage with samples of the sandy soil on which they live produces a close color match.

In one study undertaken in North Africa 25 out of 33 larks were found to match the color of the soil where they were living. This figure improved to 20 out of a total of 22 birds when comparisons were made only in the breeding season. This suggests that the larks are especially well adapted to suit the background color of their breeding habitat, which would obviously have the most survival value. In Europe, however, the match is not as good. Only 8 larks out of a sample of 14 birds matched the soil. This is probably because the vegetation in Europe is thicker than in North Africa and the larks' nests are not surrounded by bare soil.

From North Africa eastward, the plumage of sand larks also matches soil colors. In Arabia, for instance, where there are patches of black lava in the sand, there are two subspecies of desert larks, *Ammomanes deserti*. The dark subspecies is found in a region dominated by lava and the light subspecies occurs in sandy regions.

CRESTED PORCUPINE

T HE PORCUPINES OF EURASIA AND AFRICA do not usually climb, whereas those porcupines native to North and South America spend much of their time in trees. For this reason, and because of other differences, North and South American porcupines are placed in a separate family, Erethizontidae, which is discussed in the article "Tree porcupine."

One of the largest rodents, the crested porcupine grows up to 3 feet (90 cm) long excluding its 3–6¾-inch (8–17 cm) tail, and it may weigh up to 60 pounds (27 kg). It is brownish black with a whitish band around the neck, and is heavily built with short, stout legs. The body is covered with two kinds of quills (spines). One set is short and stout, the other long and slender, and both are banded black-and-white. The long quills may be over 1 foot (30 cm) long and ¼ inch (0.6 cm) in diameter. On the head and neck is a crest of long white bristles with brown bases. The quills on the rump are black, whereas those on the tail are white. The tufts of short quills that grow on the crested porcupine's tail are hollow and may be

rattled as a warning when the animal feels threatened. Though its eyesight is poor, the crested porcupine has an excellent sense of hearing and smell.

The crested porcupine ranges across North Africa, from Morocco east to Sudan and southern Egypt, and is also found south of the Sahara. It also occurs in Turkey, Sicily and Italy, where it may have been introduced by humans. It is one of eight species in the genus *Hystrix*, all of which are similar, and which are distributed from South Africa through southern Asia to Indonesia. There are seven more related species of Old World porcupines. There are two species that resemble *Hystrix*, four species of African brush-tailed porcupines and a species native to Borneo, the long-tailed porcupine, *Trichys fasciculata*.

Rodents that gnaw bones

Despite their unusual spiny appearance, porcupines are rodents and their quills are merely modified hairs. As with all rodents, they have a pair of stout, chisel-like incisor teeth in both

Crested porcupine quills can exceed 1 foot (30 cm) in length. Although they are not venomous, the quills are barbed and often work their way deep into a predator's flesh as it attempts to dislodge them.

upper and lower jaws. The incisors grow continuously at the roots and need constant use, not only to keep them sharp but also to wear them down at the crowns to prevent them from growing too long. This partly accounts for the crested porcupine's habit of gnawing bones, a habit that it shares with other rodents, including certain squirrels and dormice. Bone-gnawing rodents also benefit from the lime and phosphorus salts present in bones.

Nocturnal herbivores

Crested porcupines live singly or in pairs. They live chiefly on rocky hills with good undergrowth and spend the day in holes in the ground

The crested porcupine is strictly nocturnal. It forages alone or in pairs, feeding mainly on roots, tubers, bulbs and fallen fruits.

or among rocks, emerging at night to forage for roots, tubers, bulbs, bark and fallen fruits. In the course of one night a solitary porcupine may cover over 9 miles (15 km) in its search for food. If it is traveling over familiar territory, the porcupine will follow established paths, leaving feces at specific points during its journey.

The crested porcupine will often attack crops of corn growing near woodland, particularly during the late summer when the corn cobs are ripening. The cobs are too high for the porcupine to reach on all fours, and it must stand on its hind legs and press on the corn with its forefeet in order to bend the plant over. Ripe grapes are another of the porcupine's favorite foods, and the animal can cause considerable damage to vineyards. Near cultivated land crested porcupines can become a pest to crops and may be killed by farmers. However, the species is not threatened.

CRESTED PORCUPINE

CLASS	**Mammalia**
ORDER	**Rodentia**
FAMILY	**Hystricidae**
GENUS AND SPECIES	***Hystrix cristata***

ALTERNATIVE NAMES
African crested porcupine; African porcupine

WEIGHT
22–60 lb. (10–27 kg)

LENGTH
Head and body: 2–3 ft. (60–90 cm); tail: 3–6¾ in. (8–17 cm)

DISTINCTIVE FEATURES
Stocky body; short, stout legs with powerful claws on forefeet; small eyes and ears; blackish or dark brown fur; black-and-white quills (spines) on back and tail; crest of white bristles from forehead to shoulders

DIET
Roots, tubers, bulbs, fallen fruits, bark, root crops, corn and cucumbers; sometimes dried carrion and bones

BREEDING
Age at first breeding: 18 months or more; breeding season: March–December; number of young: 1 to 4; gestation period: 110–120 days; breeding interval: usually 1 or 2 litters per year

LIFE SPAN
Up to 15 years

HABITAT
Forest, scrub, bush and rocky mountains

DISTRIBUTION
Italy and Sicily, Asian Turkey (Anatolia), North Africa, sub-Saharan Africa south to Angola and Tanzania

STATUS
Generally uncommon, but not under threat

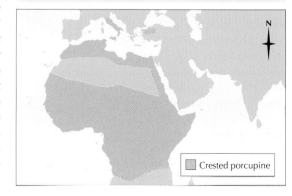

Crested porcupine

Crested porcupines are extremely protective of their young and aggressively defend them against predators.

If no natural hollows or holes abandoned by other animals are available, crested porcupines dig their own burrows using the claws on their powerful front feet. The burrows are usually made within a wood or among scrub. Each burrow has several entrances concealed by thick vegetation. A crested porcupine will occupy the same burrow for several months if undisturbed, although it may dig more tunnels over time.

Courtship and mating

Prior to mating, a male and female crested porcupine stand close together, rattling the quills on their tails and licking one another. The female indicates her acceptance of the male by raising her tail and placing it flat against her back. This prompts the male to approach her, standing on his hind legs to avoid her spines. The coupling itself rarely lasts for more than 5–6 seconds.

Crested porcupines breed early in the year. After a gestation of 110–120 days, up to four fully developed young are born in a nest of leaves, grasses and roots. Their eyes are open at birth, and the quills are soft and flexible, though they harden within the next 10 days. The young porcupines are at first striped black-and-white. Crested porcupines live for up to 15 years, or about 20 years in captivity.

Deadly quills

It is doubtful whether porcupines suffer seriously from predators. Only the larger carnivores such as leopards and Cape hunting dogs are able successfully to attack them, and even these usually do so only when suitable prey is scarce. Many predators of porcupines abandon their prey with quills painfully embedded in the mouth and paws. Young porcupines are more easily taken. Experienced predators learn to flip a porcupine over and attack the soft underbelly.

If it is threatened, a crested porcupine will bare its teeth, growl and stamp its forefeet. It raises its mane and shakes the hollow quills on its tail by way of warning to its attacker. If this behavior does not deter the predator, the porcupine will turn around and rapidly back into its aggressor, or spring sideways onto it. The porcupine's quills are only loosely rooted in its skin and so they easily become detached and embedded in the predator's flesh, driven in by the weight of the porcupine's body.

Contrary to popular belief, the quills are not shot at the predator. Because of their barbed points, any movement causes the quills to work their way in ever deeper, and they have been known to penetrate vital organs such as the heart. Some dead animals have been found with porcupine quills embedded in them up to a depth of 4 inches (10 cm). The quills themselves are not venomous, but the wounds that they inflict may turn septic and in turn can prove fatal for the predator.

The main danger to crested porcupines comes from humans. In some parts of Africa, porcupines are hunted for food and the animals have little defense against human hunters.

CRICKET

CRICKETS ARE FOUND virtually worldwide, and the numerous species are divided into three main groups. The family Gryllidae, or typical crickets, includes more than 2,200 species. The family Gryllotalpidae, or mole crickets, contains more than 50 species. The family Tettigoniidae, or katydids, consists of more than 5,000 species. The members of this final group are closely related to the Gryllidae, but are not true crickets. Misleadingly, they are commonly referred to as bush crickets and sometimes as long-horned grasshoppers. The katydids are discussed in greater detail elsewhere.

Body structure

Typical crickets resemble grasshoppers, locusts and katydids. They have very long hind legs with powerful muscles that enable them to leap high into the air. The hind legs of all these insects are equipped with sharp barbs, providing them with a means of defense.

The typical crickets differ from grasshoppers and locusts, but resemble katydids, in having long, threadlike antennae. These are used to probe into cracks and under leaves for food. Crickets also use their long antennae as organs of smell and taste. In particular they use their antennae to pick up chemical emanations from potential sexual partners.

Typical crickets produce sound in the same way as katydids. Like their relatives, the crickets have hearing organs, or insect ears, on the tibiae of each foreleg. A membrane in each organ picks up sound vibrations and transfers them to the nervous system via an auditory nerve.

Most species of typical crickets are not strong fliers and prefer to use their strong hind legs when covering long distances. Indeed, not all typical crickets have wings, but those that do have two pairs. The tough forewings are situated above the abdomen. When not in use, they are held flat over the cricket's back to protect the more fragile hind wings.

Prefer warm environments

The house cricket, *Acheta domesticus*, probably originated in North Africa and southwestern Asia. In temperate climates it is usually found in

Adult field crickets, Gryllus campestris, hibernate in winter burrows, emerging in spring. Like the rest of their family, they look like grasshoppers and locusts, but with much longer antennae.

CRICKETS

PHYLUM	**Arthropoda**
CLASS	**Insecta**
ORDER	**Orthoptera**
FAMILY	**Gryllidae**
GENUS	**Many, including *Acheta* and *Gryllus***
SPECIES	**More than 2,200, including house cricket, *Acheta domesticus*; and field and wood crickets, genus *Gryllus***

LENGTH
Varies according to species. House cricket: about ¾ in. (2 cm). Field cricket: about 1 in. (2.5 cm). Wood cricket: ½ in. (1.3 cm).

DISTINCTIVE FEATURES
Resemble grasshoppers and locusts, but with long, threadlike antennae; strong, elongated hind legs; 2 pairs of wings folded around back, but some species wingless; large ovipositor (female only); 1 pair of jointed appendages at tip of abdomen; usually brown or black in color

DIET
Mainly plant matter, supplemented with small insects and other invertebrates; also domestic scraps (some species only)

BREEDING
Age at first breeding: about 1–2 years; breeding season: summer or all year, depending on species; number of eggs: usually 40 to 170

LIFE SPAN
Varies according to species and environment

HABITAT
Grassland, woodland, farmland and arid country. House cricket: often associated with human habitation.

DISTRIBUTION
Virtually worldwide; absent from coldest regions

STATUS
Generally common

House crickets thrive in buildings and near human habitation. They scavenge scraps of food and detritus.

The field cricket (genus *Gryllus*) ranges across the warm temperate regions of Europe, south to North Africa. It is nearly 1 inch (2.5 cm) long and shiny black with pale yellow markings at the bases of the forewings. The field cricket has a large head compared to the rest of its body. The hind wings are so reduced that it cannot fly. It lives on heaths, preferring warm south-facing slopes. The adults hibernate in burrows that they dig out with their large powerful jaws. The wood cricket, in the same genus as the field cricket, is small, brown and less than ½ inch (1.3 cm) long. It ranges across the southern half of Europe, into western Asia and North Africa. It has no hind wings and is unable to fly.

One of the best known mole crickets is the common mole cricket of the genus *Gryllotalpa*. It lacks the long antennae and jumping hind legs of the typical crickets, and its forelegs are modified for digging. The hind wings are fully developed. The species is dark brown, covered with a fine velvety hair, and 1½ inches (4 cm) long. It occurs in Europe, western Asia and North Africa.

Omnivorous diet

Crickets are mainly vegetarian but will take insects and other invertebrates, the proportion varying not only with the species but also with circumstances. Some species will eat dead animal food as well as household scraps. Such an omnivorous diet has made it easy for the house cricket to live alongside humans. The mole crickets are often regarded as agricultural pests and can

places that are protected and warm, such as buildings and rotting garbage heaps. These habitats provide the insect with continual heat. The house cricket is brown, approximately ¾ inches (2 cm) long and has fully developed wings and long hind legs. It forages at night for scraps of food and other organic detritus.

pulse of sound in a chirp, or a combination of these factors, change the meaning of the cricket's message.

Crickets sing for a variety of reasons. Two males in dispute over territory or over a female will face each other, raise their hind wings and emit a certain pattern of chirps and pulses. If neither male backs down, a fight may take place. This is at least partially ritualized, but can lead to the death of one of the participants. The loser is frequently eaten by the victor.

Calling for mates

Songs are especially important during the mating season, and each species has its own mating song. It is almost exclusively the males that do the singing, using their songs as a means of guiding females to them. The choice of location for making the song is critical. Male crickets may position themselves in discarded bottles and cans to amplify the sound of their singing. Alternatively, they set themselves on a leaf in order to be free from ground litter, which muffles sound.

Many of the crickets and their relatives have evolved superb camouflage. The stone cricket lives in the rocky landscapes of South Africa.

sometimes do damage to root crops. However, their bad reputation is undeserved because for the most part they feed on other insects.

Cricket songs

Most members of the order Orthoptera inhabit areas of dense foliage, and such habitats conceal them for much of the time from both predators and other members of their species. Consequently, they have evolved a sophisticated system of calls in order to communicate with one another. Each species of cricket has evolved a specific set of sounds.

A cricket's characteristic song is produced by stridulation, the act of rubbing a finely toothed vein on the right forewing against the hind edge of the left forewing. Polished membranes on the wings act as resonators and amplify the sound. Typical crickets and katydids raise their wings during stridulation. By varying the height of the wings from the body, these insects can make the source of the sound appear to be farther away from or nearer to the listener. If a cricket senses danger, it alters the pitch of its call in this way and so throws its voice, thereby creating the impression that it is in a different location.

Each song is made up of several significant factors, which vary according to the message that the cricket is conveying. The repetition of a chirp, the variations in the length of time between each

If the female accepts the male, he climbs onto her back so that their abdomens are joined at the rear, and they mate. The male cricket deposits his sperm directly into the female in the form of small capsules, known as spermatophores. These are held by the female within her spermatheca, a sperm-retaining structure. As her eggs pass along the oviduct, the female releases the sperm to fertilize them. The females of some cricket species are prevented from mating again after they have mated once, due to the large masses of eggs inside them. The egg masses reduce the females' hearing ability and they remain deaf to male mating calls until they have laid the eggs.

The female field cricket lays her eggs in May–June by inserting them into the ground with her long ovipositor. The young hatch several weeks later, after which they overwinter, completing development and engaging in reproduction the following season. The adults die in July and August. The female wood cricket lays her eggs in the fall, the young hatching the following spring and hibernating to complete their growth in the second summer. Wood crickets take two years to develop into adults, which means that in any year a proportion of the species is still immature and another is adult. The two groups seldom interbreed.

CROAKER

ROAKER IS THE NAME given to about 270 species of fish present in most of the world's tropical and more temperate oceans. They usually have a rounded snout and one or two short spines in the anal fin. Their two dorsal fins appear to be separate, but are in fact joined at the base of the second fin. Some species of croakers also have a number of small barbels under the chin.

A varied family

Feeding habits vary greatly among the 70 genera of croakers in the family Sciaenidae. As a result there is considerable variation in mouth size. The fast-swimming sea trouts of the genus *Cynoscion* have large, angled mouths in which to catch fish. The black drum, *Pogonias chromis*, feeds on hard-shelled invertebrates. Its mouth is relatively small but it has large pharyngeal (throat) teeth for crushing the shells of its prey.

The totoaba, *Totoaba macdonaldi*, of the Gulf of California, grows up to 220 pounds (100 kg). However, most croakers weigh only a fraction of this. The Atlantic croaker may weigh less than 2 pounds (0.9 kg).

Some croakers favor northern European waters, while the meager croaker, or redfish, *Sciaena aquila*, is found along the estuaries and sandy shores of European and African coasts. The Atlantic croaker, *Micropogon undulatus*,

occurs in coastal waters from Massachusetts south to Argentina. These fish lay small eggs, each of which contains an oil globule that allows it to float to the water's surface. Most croakers are exploited as food fish.

Submarine choristers

Croakers are best known for their ability to make noises. They are not the only fish to produce sounds, but as a family they have a highly distinctive vocabulary of noises and well-developed ear bones. Many croaker species live in murky estuarine waters in which visibility is poor. Aural communication and navigation by sound are necessarily more useful than eyesight to fish in such an environment.

The sounds that croakers make are produced in most instances by the vibration of muscles. They are amplified by the highly specialized, elaborate swim bladder, which acts as a resonator. In some species the muscles are attached directly to the surface of the swim bladder. In others they are attached to the body wall. However, the technique for producing sounds is similar in all croakers: by contraction and relaxation, at a rate of about 24 contractions a second, the muscle is made to vibrate in a similar way to the strings of a guitar. The sounds have been variously described as drumming, humming, purring, whistling, creaking, croak-

The yellowfin croaker, Umbrina roncador, is native to the Gulf of California, Mexico. Croakers, or drums, are named for their ability to produce sounds by resonating their highly modified swim bladders with special muscles.

ing, hissing and snorting. Some species are commonly known as drums because of the sound they make. Those croakers that lack a swim bladder may produce a chattering sound by rubbing their pharyngeal teeth together.

In some croakers the sounds are relatively feeble, but the loudest species has been heard 6 feet (1.8 m) above the sea on the deck of a boat, while the fish was calling from a depth of nearly 60 feet (18 m). In Malaysia fishers can locate croakers by sound alone. Croakers introduced into an aquarium cease to make sounds once they are accustomed to their surroundings.

Sound production increases at specific times, for example during the mating season and after sunset. Some species have a dawn chorus while others have both dawn and dusk choruses. In some species only the males drum, while in others both sexes do so. Studies made of the weakfish, *Cynoscion regalis*, in Delaware Bay, Ohio, revealed that drumming activity increased markedly in mid-May to a peak that was maintained until July. The drumming ceased altogether in August. During the course of a day, drumming activity was at its lowest in the early morning, then rose in the early evening, staying at this level until the following morning. The peaks in drumming activity during the year were found to tally with the periods of maximum male and female reproductive readiness.

The sounds of the sea

In the past scientists believed that fish were unable to hear and that they made no sounds. However, it has since been proved that even fish in which the swim bladder is not directly connected to the bones of the inner ear can respond to frequencies of 13–3,000 cycles per second. Those fish that do have a connection to the inner ear can respond to frequencies of 16–10,000 cycles per second. The noises they make are well within these ranges, but are mainly low notes. The sounds are put to many uses in different species of fish: to enable members of a shoal to keep in touch with each other, possibly as an echo sounder for depth, and during the breeding season to communicate with potential mates.

In the past the depths of the seas and oceans were presumed to be silent. With the development of underwater listening devices during World War II, this notion was disproved. Submarine hydrophone operators often mistook the sounds made by croakers for distant enemy vessels. As well as the whales, dolphins, porpoises, croakers and other fish known to break the underwater silence, it has been discovered that even some shrimps and prawns can produce underwater sounds.

CROAKERS

CLASS	**Osteichthyes**
ORDER	**Perciformes**
FAMILY	**Sciaenidae**
GENUS	**About 70, including *Aplodinotus*, *Micropogon*, *Roncador*, *Umbrina*, *Totoaba*, *Pogonias*, *Cynoscion* and *Sciaena***
SPECIES	**About 270, including freshwater drum, *A. grunniens*; Atlantic croaker, *M. undulatus*; spotfin croaker, *R. stearnsi*; yellowfin croaker, *U. roncador*; totoaba, *T. macdonaldi*; and black drum, *P. chromis***

ALTERNATIVE NAMES
Drum (certain species only); sea trout (*Cynoscion* only)

WEIGHT
Up to 220 lb. (100 kg), usually much less

LENGTH
12–80 in. (0.3–2 m)

DISTINCTIVE FEATURES
Rounded snout; 2 dorsal fins; small barbels under chin (certain species only); 1 or 2 short spines in anal fin; enlarged swim bladder used to produce noise

DIET
Invertebrates and other fish

BREEDING
Poorly known

LIFE SPAN
Up to about 10 years

HABITAT
Mainly shallow, coastal waters; a few species in fresh water

DISTRIBUTION
Coastal waters virtually worldwide; freshwater species occur in Americas

STATUS
Generally abundant or common; critically endangered: *T. macdonaldi*

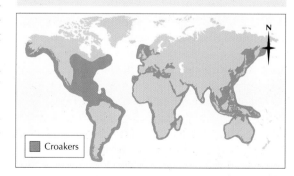

Croakers

CROCODILE

CROCODILES AND THEIR CLOSE RELATIVES, alligators, caimans and gharials, are the sole survivors of the great group of reptiles, the Archosauria, that included the dinosaurs. The crocodile family itself includes the dwarf crocodile, *Osteolaemus tetraspis*, and false gharial, *Tomistoma schlegeli*, as well as the dozen or so species of true crocodiles.

The shape of a crocodile's snout offers one means of distinguishing between species. It is long and broad in the Nile crocodile, *Crocodylus niloticus*, the best-known species, short in the Indian marsh crocodile, or mugger, *C. palustris*, and long and narrow in the false gharial. The differences between crocodiles and alligators are discussed in the article "Alligator."

As with many large, powerful animals, the size of crocodiles has often been exaggerated. There is reliable evidence for the Nile crocodile reaching 20 feet (6 m), and specimens of the American crocodile, *C. acutus*, and Orinoco crocodile, *C. intermedius*, have been measured at 23 feet (7 m). At the other extreme, the Congo subspecies of dwarf crocodile, *O. t. osborni*, has

never been recorded as exceeding 45 inches (1.1 m). Crocodiles have been hunted intensively, and large individuals of most species have now become rare.

Temperature regulation

Crocodiles are found in the warmer parts of the world, including the tropical and subtropical regions of Africa, Asia, Australia and the Americas. Unlike alligators, they are often found in brackish (slightly salty) water and have even been known to swim out to sea. The Indo-Pacific crocodile, *C. porosus*, is also known as the saltwater, or estuarine, crocodile because it is particularly common in brackish habitats. It has colonized many of the islands that lie between Asia and Australia.

Reptiles such as crocodiles are said to be cold-blooded because they cannot keep their body temperatures within fine limits in the way that mammals and birds can. A reptile's body temperature is usually within a few degrees of that of its surroundings. It cannot shiver to keep warm or sweat to keep cool. However, many

Crocodiles often rest with their mouths wide open. This may be to regulate body heat, or to allow the mouth to dry out, thereby reducing the chance of fungal infections. Pictured is the American crocodile.

CROCODILES

CLASS	**Reptilia**
ORDER	**Crocodylia**
FAMILY	**Crocodylidae**

GENUS AND SPECIES **14 species, including Nile crocodile, *Crocodylus niloticus*; and American crocodile, *C. acutus***

LENGTH
C. *niloticus*: up to 20 ft. (6 m); usually less than 16½ ft. (5 m). *C. acutus*: up to 16½ ft. (5 m), usually less than 13 ft. (4 m).

DISTINCTIVE FEATURES
Armor of tough scales and osteoderms (bony deposits); broad snout; long, muscular tail; teeth large and (unlike in alligators) positioned in line; 4th pair of teeth in lower jaw enlarged and protrude when mouth shut

DIET
C. *niloticus*: wide range of mammals, reptiles, fish and invertebrates. *C. acutus*: mainly fish; also turtles, frogs and mollusks.

BREEDING
Age at first breeding: 12–15 years (*C. niloticus*), 5–10 years (*C. acutus*); breeding season: summer or dry season; number of eggs: 15 to 80; hatching period: about 90 days, depending on temperature

LIFE SPAN
Up to 50 years

HABITAT
Rivers, marshes, swamps, lakes and water holes

DISTRIBUTION
C. *niloticus*: much of Africa, except north and south; Madagascar. *C. acutus*: southern Florida; Mexico south to northern Colombia and Venezuela; Caribbean islands.

STATUS
C. *niloticus*: common. *C. acutus*: vulnerable.

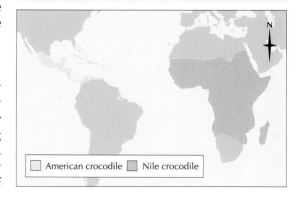

American crocodile ☐ Nile crocodile ■

The Indo-Pacific, or saltwater, crocodile often occurs in the slightly salty water of estuaries and swamps. By staying submerged in the heat of the day, crocodiles maintain their body temperature within certain limits.

reptiles, including crocodiles, keep their body temperatures from varying too much by following a daily routine to avoid extremes of temperature.

Crocodiles emerge from the water at sunrise to bask in the sun. When their bodies have warmed up, they move either into the shade or back into the water to escape the midday heat. In the late afternoon they bask again, returning to the water by nightfall. Water retains heat more effectively than air, and so crocodiles conserve their body heat by staying underwater at night.

Stones in their stomachs

When crocodiles leave the water, they generally stay near the bank, although occasionally they wander some distance in search of new water and can cause great consternation by appearing in towns. They are generally sluggish but, considering their bulky bodies and relatively short legs, are capable of unexpected bursts of speed. Crocodiles have two distinct gaits. The first is a high walk, in which the body is lifted well off the ground with the legs under the body. The second method is the low walk, which is similar to that used by most other reptiles. In this mode, the crocodile's legs are splayed out and the belly remains close to the ground. This gait is usually adopted only over short distances.

There are two other forms of terrestrial locomotion used by crocodiles. Most can trot and smaller or young crocodiles can gallop at speeds of up to 10 miles per hour (16 km/h) when required. Any increase in speed results in a collapse of leg synchronization and the crocodile ends up sliding on its belly using its legs as paddles. This final method of locomotion is most often used when sliding down an embankment into a river, lake or pool.

Crocodiles float very low in the water, often with little more than their eyes and nostrils showing. They habitually carry several pounds of stones in their stomachs, which help to stabilize their bodies. The stones lie in the stomach, below the center of gravity, and counterbalance the buoyant lungs. This is particularly useful when the crocodiles are fairly young as they are top-heavy and cannot float easily at the surface.

Kill by brute force

During their first year, young crocodiles feed on small animals, including frogs, dragonflies, crabs and even mosquito larvae. A hatchling crocodile swims stealthily toward its prey and then pounces, snapping at its victim with a sideways movement of the jaws. This movement is necessary because the crocodile's eyes are at the side of its head. Young crocodiles have also been seen cornering insect larvae by curving their bodies and tails around them.

As a crocodile grows, the amount of insects in its diet decreases, and it begins to eat water snails and fish. When adult, it continues to catch fish but turns increasingly to trapping mammals and birds. Adult crocodiles capture their prey by lying in wait near game trails and water holes. When a victim approaches, the crocodile seizes it and drags it underwater or knocks it over with a blow from its tail or head. Once the victim is pulled into the water, the crocodile has a definite advantage. Drowning soon stills the victim's struggles and, grasping a limb in its jaws, the crocodile may roll over and over so that the victim is dismembered.

Dangerous to humans?

Crocodiles are widely regarded as being a threat to humans, though this reputation is only partly justified. It may be that only certain individuals attack people. In parts of Africa, crocodiles are not regarded as a menace at all, while elsewhere palisades have to be erected at the edge of streams and rivers to allow people to fetch water in safety. It seems that crocodiles are likely to be more aggressive when their streams and pools dry up so they cannot escape, or when they are guarding their young.

In a crocodile's nest

The Nile crocodile breeds when it is 12–15 years old, by which time it has grown to a length of 7–10 feet (2–3 m). The full-grown males stake out their territories along the banks and share them

The Cuban crocodile, Crocodylus rhombifer, is endangered due to a long history of being hunted and, more recently, to interbreeding with American crocodiles. Hybrids of the two species may now outnumber the pure Cuban species.

Large species such as the Nile crocodile hunt mammals by hiding near a spot where prey comes to drink. When prey is close enough, the crocodile rushes forward and seizes it, dragging it back into the water for the kill.

the female, sometimes the male also, takes the hatchlings in the mouth to carry them to water. The hatchlings disperse when 6–8 weeks old. Young Nile crocodiles are about 1 foot (30 cm) long at hatching and for their first 7 years grow at a rate of about 10 inches (25 cm) a year.

The female crocodile has to be permanently on her guard as many animals feed on crocodile eggs and hatchling crocodiles. The chief predators are monitor lizards, which are bold enough to dig underneath the crocodile as she lies over her nest. Baby crocodiles are also eaten by mongooses, turtles, herons, eagles, predatory fish and other crocodiles. Predators of adult crocodiles include lions and leopards, and hippos attack crocodiles in defense of their young.

Crocodile tears

The phrase "to shed crocodile tears" means to make a false appearance of showing grief or sympathy. The origin of the phrase probably stems from a misguided observation. When James Hawkins stated that "many crocodils" encountered during his explorations throughout the Americas in 1565 "cry and sobbe" he was probably observing osmoregulation. This is a process whereby the balance of water and salts in the body is maintained. Excess salt can be excreted, as a strong solution, from salt glands in the tongue and skin as well as through the urine and feces. Hawkins probably observed this saline solution exuding near to a crocodile's eyes and mistook it for tears.

with younger males and females. They defend the territories by fighting, which may sometimes end in one contestant being killed. Prior to mating, the male crocodile approaches a female and displays to her by thrashing the water with his snout and tail. The two then swim in circles with the male on the outside. He tries to get near to the female so that he can put a forelimb over her body and mate.

Female Nile and marsh crocodiles dig pits 2 feet (60 cm) deep for their nests, and the Indo-Pacific crocodile of northern Australia and Southeast Asia makes a mound of leaves. The nests are built near water and shade, where the female can guard her brood and keep herself cool. During the incubation period she stays by the nest, defending it against predators. These include other crocodiles, although in colonies nests may be only a few yards apart. Up to 90 eggs are laid, depending on species, during the summer or dry season. They hatch about 3–4 months later in the rainy season, when insect prey is plentiful.

The hatchling crocodiles begin to grunt before hatching. This is the signal for the female to uncover the nest. The hatchlings climb out and

Sustainable harvesting

More than half of the world's 21 crocodilian species are currently threatened. However, extensive efforts by conservation organizations, in coordination with representatives from the exotic leather industry, have helped to bring several species back from the brink of extinction. Sustainable harvesting programs, whereby eggs and hatchlings are removed from the wild to be reared in ranches for leather production, have so far proved to be an effective means of crocodile conservation. A proportion of the stock of crocodiles is returned to the wild once it is past the vulnerable hatchling stage and a portion of the profits from the sale of skins is donated to the relevant conservation authority. In this way both the target species and its habitat may be maintained indefinitely.

CROSSBILL

Crossbills have unique, asymmetrical bills. The twisted mandibles (bill-halves) operate rather like tweezers to remove the seeds from pine cones.

CROSSBILLS ARE ACROBATIC FINCHES with unique bills in which the upper and lower mandibles, or bill-halves, cross over one other. The male common, or red, crossbill, *Loxia curvirostra*, has brick red or carmine plumage with blackish wings and tail; the females are olive or greenish gray. The two-barred crossbill, *L. leucoptera*, is similar but with a pair of distinctive white bars on its wings. The parrot crossbill, *L. pytyopsittacus*, also resembles the common crossbill but has a larger bill and thicker neck.

The common crossbill breeds in the Northern Hemisphere from Alaska east to Newfoundland in North America and from Scotland eastward to Korea. It ranges as far south as Mexico, northwestern Africa and southern Asia. Like other crossbills, it is found only where there are forests of coniferous trees. Consequently, the species has isolated populations in many places, including Spain, among the localized areas of Scots firs and Mediterranean pines, and Morocco, where there are Aleppo pines.

The two-barred crossbill is found in Canada, Siberia and northern Russia. The parrot crossbill is found in pine forests in Scandinavia, the Baltic states and northern Russia. A fourth species of crossbill, the Scottish crossbill, *L. scotica*, is the least numerous and has a relatively restricted range. It occurs only in the Caledonian forests of northern Scotland. The Scottish crossbill has a bill intermediate in size between those of the common and parrot crossbills.

Seed splitters

The primary food source of crossbills is the seeds from the cones of pine, larch, spruce, fir and other conifers. Crossbills occasionally eat other seeds such as apple, hawthorn, thrift and crowberry, but usually only when cones are in short supply. Some insects, especially those living in galls, such as gall wasp larvae, are also eaten.

Crossbills are energetic feeders and feed in small flocks, in common with many species of finch. They take seeds from the cones while they are still on the tree. The birds climb onto the cones, often using their bills as an extra support, in the manner of parrots and parakeets. Crossbills usually eat fallen cones only toward the end of winter or in spring when food is running short. The birds use their crossed bill to wrench off the scales and split them vertically, while the seed is extracted with the tongue. Crossbills use their feet to hold the cone steady while they work at it with their bill and tongue, though the extent to which they do this depends on the leg structure and body weight of the species.

The common crossbill occurs in a broad band across the northern regions of North America, Europe and Asia. Adult males are red to varying degrees, and the females are greenish gray.

COMMON CROSSBILL

CLASS	**Aves**
ORDER	**Passeriformes**
FAMILY	**Fringillidae**
GENUS AND SPECIES	***Loxia curvirostra***

ALTERNATIVE NAME
Red crossbill

LENGTH
**Head to tail: 6–6⅔ in. (15–17 cm);
wingspan: 10⅔–12 in. (27–30 cm)**

DISTINCTIVE FEATURES
**Strong bill with upper and lower mandibles
(bill-halves) twisted over one another;
large, thickset head; notch in center of tail.
Male: scarlet to orange red with brownish
wings. Female: greenish gray. Young: dark
brown streaks on underparts.**

DIET
**Seeds of coniferous trees, especially pine,
larch, spruce and fir; occasionally also
insects and seeds of deciduous trees**

BREEDING
**Age at first breeding: 6 months; breeding
season: almost all year; number of eggs:
3 or 4; incubation period: 14–15 days;
fledging period: 20–25 days; breeding
interval: 1 or 2 broods per year**

LIFE SPAN
Up to 7 years

HABITAT
Pine, spruce and fir forest, often in uplands

DISTRIBUTION
**Mainly in northern North America and
Eurasia; also in Rocky Mountains, central
Mexico, Mediterranean, northwestern
Africa and Central and southern Asia**

STATUS
**Common; size of populations fluctuates
dramatically according to food availability**

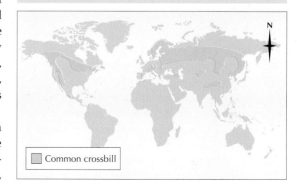

Common crossbill

Bill size and seed availability

Ornithologists believe that the variety of bill size displayed in crossbill species has evolved in response to the diversity of conifer cone structures and seed sizes. The availability of conifer seeds in times of food scarcity is also thought to have affected the evolution of the species' bills.

A crossbill's ability to open one kind of cone and not another depends on the strength and size of its bill, and it has been found that different crossbills prefer different cones. The size of the bill and the toughness of the preferred cone are related. Whereas the common crossbill is best able to deal with spruce and larch, the more heavily billed parrot crossbill feeds mainly on harder pine cones. The two-barred crossbill, which possesses a small bill, lives on the small, soft cones of larch. The Scottish crossbill feeds primarily on certain pines.

Research on common crossbills in North America suggests that there may be six separate forms, each with slightly different feeding preferences, bill sizes and vocalizations. For example, the crossbills of central Mexico have the largest bills, which are adapted to feeding on the large, hard-covered cones of the ponderosa and Apache pines.

Crossbill irruptions

Crossbills are subject to marked fluctuations in abundance. Their dependence on pine, spruce, fir and larch cones for food means that they have to move about in search of suitable supplies and that populations vary from year to year, depending on the quality of cone crops. Usually the crossbills do not move far, but every few years they irrupt, that is to say, there is a dramatic increase in a local population of the birds. The irruptions occur when a small crop of cones follows a good one. In the year of plenty the crossbills flourish and most of the young survive their first winter to breed and increase the population in the following spring. In that year there is a shortage of food for this large population and many birds are forced to leave and seek food elsewhere.

Occasionally there are crossbill irruptions in the British Isles, when large numbers of crossbills fly across the North Sea from Scandinavia. This situation is more likely to develop when there are northeasterly winds blowing from Norway to Britain at the time of the crossbills' movement. After an irruption, immigrant crossbills breed in the British Isles, especially in southeast England. These new populations tend to die out within a few years. However, small populations have become established in this way in several parts of England, Scotland and Wales.

Straight-billed chicks

Crossbills build their nests in trees on the edge of forests and beside rides and clearings, never in dense forest. Thin twigs, moss, grasses and other materials are made into a ragged nest by the female. The male accompanies his mate on collecting trips, although he only rarely carries any material. The female uses twigs as a foundation for the nest, placing them in a fork near the trunk or far out among the evergreen foliage.

The clutch usually consists of three or four eggs, which are incubated by the female alone for 14–15 days. During this time she does not leave the nest; the male brings food to her. She calls when she is hungry and the male flies from his nearby perch to search for food for her.

The newly hatched chicks are very resistant to cold, and the female may leave them for an hour or more in the cold of a Scandinavian or Canadian spring. When they are about 1 week old, the chicks can control their body temperature, but before this time they chill easily and become almost lifeless when exposed to the cold. They recover in a few minutes when the female broods them. This represents a form of temporary hibernation, a pattern of behavior that has been more fully studied in the nestlings of the swift, *Apus apus*.

When they hatch, the young crossbills have conventional, symmetrical bills like those of many finches, with the mandibles meeting at the tip. It is not until after they leave the nest that the two halves of the bill begin to grow crooked and cross over. The upper mandible may cross either to the left or right of the lower.

The parrot crossbill (male, left) has a larger, stronger bill and thicker neck than other crossbills. Due to their dry, seed-based diet, all crossbills must visit water regularly to relieve their thirst.

CROW

THE CROW FAMILY CONTAINS about 115 species in 25 genera, including some of the best-known of the perching birds. Familiar corvids (members of the family Corvidae) include the ravens (10 species), magpies (about 11 species), jackdaws (2 species) and jays (about 39 species). These groups are discussed elsewhere. Species in the large genus *Corvus* are often known simply as crows, and include the carrion crow, *C. corone*, and rook, *C. frugilegus*, both of Eurasia, as well as four closely related North American species. These are the American crow (*C. brachyrhynchos*), the northwestern crow (*C. caurinus*), the Tamaulipas or Mexican crow (*C. imparatus*) and the fish crow (*C. ossifragus*). The hooded crow of Europe and Asia belongs to the same species as the carrion crow, but is a distinct form that is often regarded as a subspecies.

Cosmopolitan and adaptable

Crows have an almost worldwide distribution, though they are mostly absent from the Arctic and Antarctic, southern South America and New Zealand. The members of the genus *Corvus* have been more successful in colonizing remote islands than many other corvids. A few *Corvus* species have settled in Indonsesia, the southwest Pacific, Hawaii and the Caribbean.

Crows are most abundant in the more temperate parts of the Northern Hemisphere. They range over a wide range of habitats, including grassland, farmland, coasts, hillsides, mountains, desert, steppes and tundra, though most species are birds of wooded country. Generally crows are sedentary, but they are strong fliers and some species regularly migrate within their respective ranges. Crows are highly adaptable birds and are versatile feeders. Most species take both animal and plant foods.

Appearance and characteristics

Crows are large birds and have fairly long bills, often with a small hook at the tip. The tail is usually short or of medium length. Typical crows are entirely black, including their legs and bill, or primarily black but streaked with white, brown or gray. There is no strong distinction between the plumage of the sexes.

AMERICAN CROW

CLASS **Aves**

ORDER **Passeriformes**

FAMILY **Corvidae**

GENUS AND SPECIES *Corvus brachyrhynchos*

ALTERNATIVE NAMES
Common crow; western crow (*C. b. hesperis* only); Florida crow (*C. b. pascuus* only)

WEIGHT
Usually 15½–16 oz. (440–460 g)

LENGTH
Head to tail: 15½–19½ in. (40–50 cm); wingspan: 30–35½ in. (75–90 cm)

DISTINCTIVE FEATURES
Stout, black bill with slight hook at tip and nasal bristles at base of upper mandible (bill-half); glossy, all-black plumage

DIET
Invertebrates, amphibians, small mammals, bird eggs and nestlings, seeds, nuts, carrion, scraps and human refuse

BREEDING
Age at first breeding: 2–3 years; breeding season: February–July; number of eggs: usually 4 or 5; incubation period: about 18 days; fledging period: about 35 days; breeding interval: 1 year

LIFE SPAN
Up to at least 12 years

HABITAT
Most terrestrial habitats; favors fertile agricultural land, avoids only dense forest

DISTRIBUTION
Throughout Canada and U.S., from British Columbia east to Newfoundland and south to Baja California and Texas

STATUS
Very common

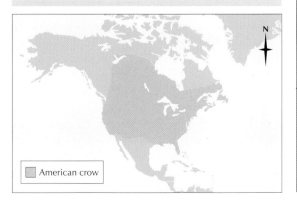

American crow

The carrion crow, 19–22 inches (48–56 cm) long, normally appears black all over. Close up, its plumage is visibly shot with blue and purple, the colors being especially apparent in strong sunlight. The American crow is similar in size, appearance and habits to the carrion crow. It gathers to sleep in roosts several thousand strong during the fall and winter. The most widespread crow in North America, the American crow is one of the few land birds to have a range that encompasses the entire width of North America. Northern populations of the species are migratory, moving south for the winter.

The fish crow is 14–16 inches (36–41 cm) in length and is therefore slightly smaller than the American crow. It has a more slender bill and a glossier plumage than its more abundant relative. The fish crow frequents coasts, rivers, marshes and coastal lowlands. Its diet is relatively specialized for a corvid, consisting of shellfish, amphibians, crabs and shrimps with

The pied crow, Corvus albus, is one of the most widespread birds in sub-Saharan Africa. It is also the only crow found in Madagascar.

Carrion crows are abundant and on the whole have benefited from human activities. There are several million breeding pairs in Europe alone.

some bird eggs and fish carrion. The species ranges along the eastern coast of the United States, from New England south to Florida, and along the coast of the Gulf of Mexico to Texas.

The hooded crow has habits similar to those of the carrion crow but is distinguished from the latter by its gray mantle and underparts. Where the ranges of these two forms overlap, the birds readily interbreed. Hybrids of the two forms show variable intermediate plumages. Zones of hybridization include southern and central Scotland and parts of central Europe, including Germany, Switzerland and Austria.

Several crow species readily feed on sown seeds and consequently are regarded as agricultural pests. Although the American crow also feeds on many insect pests, the species has been widely persecuted and is wary of humans. Crows in both Europe and the United States are persecuted by game managers because they rob the nests of gamebirds and wildfowl.

Carrion crow or rook?

The carrion crow spends most of its day feeding on the ground or perched in trees. It is often solitary or in a pair, but also forms small groups and flocks. However, these gatherings rarely exceed more than about 25 individuals. Occasionally crows associate with flocks of rooks, which are strictly social. The old British saying that one or two birds on their own are crows but in a flock are rooks, is generally accurate.

A rook can be distinguished by the gray skin at the base of the bill, the carrion crow by the black feathers on the base of its bill, although first-year rooks also have this feature. A carrion crow throws its head up and brings it down again as it caws, simultaneously depressing and fanning its tail. A rook lowers its head as it calls, so bill, neck and body are more or less horizontal. At the same time the rook holds its tail up in a fan. The flight style of both carrion crows and rooks is slow and deliberate with regular, heavy wingbeats.

Nothing wasted

Crows are typically able to feed on a wide variety of foods in many different ways, due to their inquisitiveness, strength and multipurpose bills. Plant foods taken include seeds, grasses, herbs, fruits such as cherries and apples, root crops, acorns, pine cone seeds and walnuts. Animal prey ranges from earthworms, spiders and insects, especially beetles and their larvae, to frogs, toads, shellfish, crustaceans, fish, bird eggs and nestlings, small mammals, carrion and scraps. Crows kill mainly injured or sick animals, particularly small birds and rodents.

Typical crows are opportunist omnivores. In addition to stealing eggs and nestlings from the unattended nests of other bird species, they chase gulls and smaller corvids to steal their food. This behavior is a form of parasitism. Crows also exploit unusual or seasonal food sources, such as road kills, sheep afterbirths and stranded fish.

Breeding

Carrion crows construct their nests during April. The nest is typically positioned in a stout fork of a tree, at a point from which the main branches spread, but it may also be built in a bush or on a cliff. It is built mainly, if not entirely, by the male. Nests are primarily built using twigs, with the addition of some earth and moss and a lining of materials such as grasses and wool. The nests are usually left open at the top, though in a small number of other crow species they are covered over. Many species of crow breed to take advantage of a peak in suitable food supplies for the nestlings. In England, rooks lay in March when there is an abundance of earthworms.

The female carrion crow typically lays four to five eggs, though occasionally she may produce as many as seven. The eggs are incubated by the female, which is fed on the nest by the male. They hatch in 17–19 days, the nestlings being fed at first by the female and later by both parents, which bring food in their throat-pouches. This feeding period lasts for 30–35 days. After fledging, the young carrion crows are fed for a further 4–5 weeks by both parents.

Carrion crows use communal roosts in the fall and winter, occasionally sharing the rooks' roosts. However, even where many carrion crows gather to sleep in groups of trees they number less than the roosts of American crows. The population of American crows is still high despite persecution by humans.

Few predators

The bill of a crow is strong and powerful, and the bird probably has few regular predators. Crows are strongly territorial and mob birds of prey, foxes and coyotes when they trespass onto their territory. Crows also mob the other birds that trigger this instinctive raptor-mobbing response, even attacking species such as herons and egrets that pose no direct threat to them.

Crows live for 12 or more years in captivity, and their life span in the wild is probably similar. Little study has been made of the causes of death among juvenile crows. The death rate is probably as high as it is in other bird species that have been studied: that is, 60–70 percent in the first 3–6 months.

The American crow is the largest crow in the United States. It is common throughout its range and occurs in a variety of habitats, including southwestern deserts in the winter.

CROWNED EAGLE

THE CROWNED EAGLE IS the most powerful African eagle. It measures 31–35 inches (80–90 cm) from head to tail, has a bluish gray bill and yellow feet and the legs are feathered right down to the short, heavy toes. The crowned eagle derives its name from the double crest that it can erect from the crown of its head. The crest feathers are black and white, the head and neck are olive-gray. The upperparts are generally blackish with a bluish, plumlike bloom, except for brownish areas on the wings. Immature birds are primarily white with barred and spotted underparts. The crowned eagle has the broad, rounded wings and long tail typical of eagles that live in dense forests, and is fast and agile. Its wing structure enables it to rise almost straight up into the air in the manner of another forest species, the harpy eagle, *Harpia harpyja*, of Central and South America.

Crowned eagles range across the southern half of Africa, from Ghana east to Sudan and south to South Africa. They are not found in the arid areas of southern and eastern Africa. Their natural habitat varies from dense rain forest to wooded savanna, though forests and rocky hills are preferred. Crowned eagles occasionally live at altitudes of more than 10,000 feet (3,000 m).

Although not the largest African bird of prey, the crowned eagle is the most powerful. The adult preys mainly on monkeys, snatching them from the treetops in its massive talons.

More common than supposed

The crowned eagle has long been considered rare by ornithologists, even by comparison with other eagles, which never have dense populations because each breeding pair needs a large range in which to hunt. In fact, crowned eagles are more common than was once supposed. They are easily overlooked because they fly just above or within the canopy of the trees when hunting. Moreover, unlike other large eagles, they perch within dense foliage rather than in the open on a bare branch or rocky crag. The nests are also difficult to find, frequently being hidden among trees at a considerable height. Often the only way to find a nest is to listen for the loud calls of the chick as the parents fly in with food.

Targets large prey

The crowned eagle feeds primarily on mammals. The largest animals taken are antelope, such as the forest-dwelling duikers (*Cephalophus* spp.) and suni (*Neotragus moschatus*). However, its more usual prey is monkeys, especially colobus monkeys (Colobidae) and vervet monkeys (*Cercopithecus pygerythrus*). Other prey includes hyraxes, smaller species of antelope and mongooses. Adult crowned eagles are capable of

CROWNED EAGLE

CLASS	**Aves**
ORDER	**Falconiformes**
FAMILY	**Accipitridae**
GENUS AND SPECIES	***Stephanoaetus coronatus***

ALTERNATIVE NAMES
African crowned eagle; crowned hawk-eagle

WEIGHT
7–8½ lb. (3.2–3.9 kg), female larger than male

LENGTH
Head to tail: 31–35 in. (80–90 cm); wingspan: 65–71 in. (1.65–1.8 m)

DISTINCTIVE FEATURES
Huge size; large crest; powerful, hooked bill; massive talons; broad, rounded wings; long tail. Adult: olive-gray head and neck; blackish upperparts with brown bars on wings; white or cinnamon underparts with black spots and bars. Juvenile: much lighter, whitish or sand-colored plumage.

DIET
Monkeys, antelope and other mammals; occasionally lizards and snakes; rarely birds

BREEDING
Age at first breeding: 4 years; breeding season: spring and summer; number of eggs: 1 or 2; incubation period: about 49 days; fledging period: about 70–80 days; breeding interval: usually 2 years

LIFE SPAN
Probably up to 30 years

HABITAT
Rain forest, wooded savanna and rocky hills

DISTRIBUTION
Much of sub-Saharan Africa; absent from Horn of Africa (Eritrea, Somalia and eastern Ethiopia) and much of southwest

STATUS
Uncommon

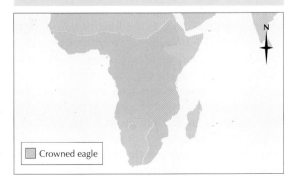

Crowned eagle

overcoming monkeys that weigh twice their own weight. They also occasionally take reptiles, such as monitor lizards and large snakes, including some venomous species. They feed on other birds only very rarely.

Immature crowned eagles have a pale, sandy white plumage. They take 4 years to reach breeding age.

Monkey-hunting strategies

The crowned eagle's impact on monkey populations has probably been exaggerated in the past. In some places the species appears to take relatively few monkeys, although monkeys certainly react with alarmed cries whenever an eagle comes into sight. Colobus monkeys are particularly vulnerable to attack while they are sunning themselves in the morning and evening.

It seems likely that monkeys can be caught only by surprise because they defend themselves vigorously if attacked and are quite capable of keeping an eagle at bay. To avoid a monkey's retaliation, the crowned eagle is reported to swoop past, grabbing the monkey by the head, and then to drop it so that it falls to the ground. The eagle then dives and kills the monkey before it is able to recover.

Prey is often killed on the forest floor, though monkeys are also taken in treetops. The crowned eagle descends on prey with legs and pelvis swung forward and often strikes its victim with enough force to kill it immediately. If the prey is not killed outright, the damage inflicted by the eagle's massive talons is usually sufficient to cause eventual death.

A crowned eagle usually kills a fully grown monkey or other good-sized mammal once every 3 or 4 days.

Courtship over the treetops

Crowned eagle nests are found high up in trees, perhaps as far as 150 feet (45 m) above ground. In open country nests can be seen from the ground but in forests they are hidden in foliage. Common nesting sites include beside streams and on steep slopes of valleys. Nests are built using dry tree branches and green fronds. Nests are used from year to year, and one in South Africa is known to have been used by successive generations of eagles for at least 75 years. Each year material is added and the structure becomes enormous. The male collects most of the material, while the female works it into the nest.

As in many other birds of prey, crowned eagle courtship displays take the form of aerial maneuvers. The male eagle describes figures of eight and circles in the air, flapping his wings just enough to gain height on a soar before plunging down again. At the top of each ascent, the male throws back his head and utters a call, which may last for 30 seconds. The steep dives and ascents of the male crowned eagle's courtship display may take place as high as 3,000 feet (915 m) above the forest canopy. The female also engages in courtship displays, though less often than the male. Her calls are less strident.

Prior to copulation the male engages in another display, running round the female with his wings raised to show his chestnut underwing coverts and striking barring. The two eagles may copulate several times a day in the nest and copulation may take place up to a year before the female lays her first egg. Incubation of the one or two eggs lasts about 7 weeks. The female does most of the incubating, while the male regularly brings her food.

The chicks spend 2½ months on the nest before flying, and during this time the elder chick apparently kills the younger. At least in the rather small number of crowned eagle nests studied, only one chick has ever survived and it is presumed that the other is killed by its nest-mate. It should be noted however that the killing of one sibling by another is the norm in eagles and is therefore not unexpected in this species.

Breeds every other year

After starting to fly, the young eagle returns to the nest to be fed. It does not stray far and returns when it sees a parent arriving with food. Later it wanders farther afield, learning to hunt for itself. It continues to be fed by the parents for 7–9 months after fledging, at which point it loses interest in them. Due to the long breeding cycle, which lasts 17–18 months, from first repairing the nest to the independence of the young, most crowned eagles breed only every other year.

Adult crowned eagles have no predators, but exceptionally their nests are attacked by baboons. The adult eagles actively defend their eggs and young, and smaller birds of prey sometimes nest near the eagles, apparently obtaining protection from their larger neighbors.

CUCKOO

THERE ARE ABOUT 130 SPECIES of cuckoos, divided into 34 genera. Of all these species, only the common cuckoo, *Cuculus canorus*, of Europe and Asia, produces the loud insistent call that has given rise to the familiar name. It is called *coucou* in French, *kuckuck* in German, *kukushka* in Russian and *kak-ko* in Japanese.

Cuckoos vary considerably in size and appearance and are systematically grouped by experts according to their geographical distribution and breeding biology rather than by any physical similarities. They are distinguished from other songbirds both by their internal anatomy and by the distinctive structure of their feet, which have four toes, two pointing forward and two back. This feature relates cuckoos to parrots and nightjars.

Cuckoos belong to two subfamilies. Members of one subfamily are found in North and South America. The other subfamily, which includes the common cuckoo, is represented from western Europe to Polynesia. Those cuckoo species belonging to this subfamily are all parasitic; the female lays her eggs in other birds' nests. It is for this habit that the cuckoos are best known, but it is not widespread in the family as a whole. Only about 50 species of cuckoos are known to lay eggs in the nests of other species.

The common cuckoo has distinctive black-and-white barring on the underparts and a gray head and neck. The tail is long and the wings are narrow, so in flight the species looks very much like a falcon or a small hawk. It can be distinguished, however, by its longer neck and by the shape of its head.

Other cuckoos are colorful by comparison with the common cuckoo. The chestnut-winged cuckoo, *Clamator coromandus*, has a magpielike tail and a black head, back and tail. The great spotted cuckoo, *Clamator glandarius*, is related to the chestnut-winged cuckoo and is similar in shape but has white spots on the wings and back. The didric cuckoo, *Chrysococcyx caprius*, of sub-Saharan Africa, has brilliant golden green plumage, except for its white underparts.

Long-distance migrants

Many cuckoos migrate over thousands of miles, leaving the Tropics to spend spring and summer in temperate regions. Common cuckoos begin to arrive in the British Isles in the first few days of April and leave during July to early September, each bird flying on its own bound for tropical Africa. The shining bronze-cuckoo, *Chrysococcyx lucidus*, of New Zealand, undertakes an even more impressive migration, journeying across

Outbreaks of eastern tent caterpillars in North American woodlands are often accompanied by an influx of cuckoos such as the yellow-billed cuckoo, Coccyzus americanus (above). The cuckoos nest in the infested areas and feed the caterpillars to their young.

In spring the male common cuckoo repeats a far-carrying ku-koo *call to attract females. This call has given rise to the names of both the species and the family to which it belongs.*

COMMON CUCKOO

CLASS	**Aves**
ORDER	**Cuculiformes**
FAMILY	**Cuculidae**
GENUS AND SPECIES	***Cuculus canorus***

ALTERNATIVE NAMES
European cuckoo; Eurasian cuckoo

LENGTH
**Head to tail: 12½–13½ in. (32–34 cm);
wingspan: 21½–23½ in. (55–60 cm)**

DISTINCTIVE FEATURES
**Sleek, hawklike profile, with long wings
and long tail; decurved bill. Adult: gray
upperparts and breast; black-and-white
barring on underparts. Juvenile: reddish
brown upperparts; dark bars on underparts.**

DIET
**Invertebrates, especially beetles, spiders,
centipedes, earthworms and insect larvae**

BREEDING
**Age at first breeding: 1 year; breeding
season: April–June; number of eggs: 1 to 25,
1 egg per host nest; incubation period:
11–12 days, by host; fledging period: about
19 days, by host; breeding interval: 1 year**

LIFE SPAN
Probably up to 12 years

HABITAT
**Grassland, woodland, steppe, savanna and
semiarid country; avoids deserts**

DISTRIBUTION
**Breeds from western Europe east to eastern
Asia and south to North Africa, northern
Middle East and northern India. Winters in
sub-Saharan Africa and Southeast Asia.**

STATUS
Common in much of range

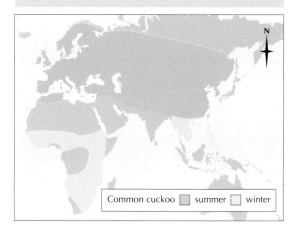

Common cuckoo ▢ summer ▢ winter

2,000 miles (3,220 km) of ocean, to and from the Solomon Islands. Scientists are still uncertain as to how the birds find their way over such vast distances. The young birds migrate from the breeding grounds several weeks after the adults have gone. This would suggest that the urge to migrate, the ability to navigate and the knowledge of the route are inherited genetically, because there is no opportunity for the young cuckoos to acquire these skills from their elders.

An appetite for insects
Cuckoos eat insects, especially the larvae, but they also eat worms, spiders, and centipedes. The beetles, flies, dragonflies, butterflies and moths that they feed on often include those harmful to agriculture, such as cockchafers, cabbage white butterflies and wireworms. In particular, cuckoos eat hairy or toxic caterpillars, including those of the cinnabar moth, which are usually left alone by other birds. Some species, such as the koels of Southeast Asia and Australia, sometimes also eat fruit.

Acquiring a host

The common cuckoo does not build a nest of its own, but lays its eggs in those of other birds, most usually songbirds. Other members of the cuckoo family do the same, as do some cowbirds and honeyguides. The female cuckoo keeps a watch for small birds building their nests. When the nest is complete, and the foster parent has laid an egg, the female cuckoo flies down to it. Choosing a time when the foster parent is away, she lifts an egg out of the nest, swallows or drops it, and very quickly lays one of her own in its place, departing before the foster parent returns.

Cuckoo eggs are sometimes found in the domed nests of willow warblers, *Phylloscopus trochilus*. It was once commonly believed that the female cuckoo laid her egg on the ground and then carried it to the nest in her bill. However, it is now known that she presses her body against the nest and ejects her egg through the entrance. In Australia and New Zealand, the shining bronze-cuckoo lays in the domed nests of wrens by forcing its head in through the entrance then out through the far wall. The bird straddles the nest, lays the egg and then leaves through the hole it has made. When the foster parent returns it repairs the gap in the nest and proceeds to treat the cuckoo's egg as one of its own. Cuckoo eggs are generally accepted by most species, although observations have shown that clutches containing a cuckoo egg are more likely to be deserted than clutches which do not.

The female cuckoo holds the egg in her oviduct for one day before laying it. This means that the cuckoo egg is one day ahead of the host egg in terms of embryonic development, and often emerges before its nestmates. This advantage is used by the cuckoo nestling to evict the other eggs and any newly hatched young. The young cuckoo maneuvers itself in the bottom of the nest so that an egg or chick becomes balanced on its back, in a hollow between the wings. It then hoists the object out of the nest, and repeats the process with any other eggs or young that are in the nest. The New World striped cuckoo, *Tapera naevia*, uses a sharp hook at the end of its bill to kill its fellow nestlings upon hatching. However, the young of some cuckoo species, such as the great spotted cuckoo, *Cuculus glandarius*, grow up alongside the host's offspring. When two female cuckoos are keeping watch in one area, they may each lay an egg in the same host nest. After a few days' jostling, the urge to empty the nest of competitors dies away and both young cuckoos proceed to live peaceably together.

If the cuckoo nestling did not evict its nestmates, they would surely die in any case, for the young cuckoo grows rapidly and its foster parents struggle to feed it. After 3 weeks it leaves the nest, which by then it has outgrown, but the foster parents continue to feed it, often perching on its back to drop insects into its gaping bill.

Egg mimickry

Surveys of clutches containing cuckoo eggs show that the cuckoo egg is often very similar in appearance to the foster parents' eggs. Experts have also discovered that in any given area cuckoos use certain host nests more than others.

The common cuckoo hatches with a hollow in its back. Into this it places the eggs or young of its host before ejecting them from the host's nest.

In Hungary, the common cuckoo mainly parasitizes the nests of the great reed warbler, *Acrocephalus arundinaceus*; the cuckoo lays greenish eggs resembling those of the warbler. In Finland, cuckoos' eggs are blue to match those of its hosts, the whinchat and redstart. Nearly all over the common cuckoo's range there are similar examples of preferences for certain hosts along with a mimicking of their eggs. It seems that a similarity in color and size reduces the chance of the eggs, and nest, being abandoned by the foster parents.

In the British Isles common cuckoo eggs differ significantly from those of their their hosts. Indeed, the eggs all tend to be of one pattern. Scientists believe the explanation for this is that a cuckoo may lay in nests of another host if it cannot find a nest of its preferred host. In Britain, where the countryside is divided into many small habitats with a large variety of possible host species, the cuckoo has not been able to form any set preferences.

Imitation and deception

It is not unusual for a common cuckoo to be mistaken for a sparrow hawk, *Accipiter nisus*, because of the similarity of shape and plumage. Bird-watchers are not the only ones to be deceived by the resemblance. When the cuckoo returns in spring, small birds will gather to mob it as if it were a hawk. There is some evidence that the species makes use of this mistake.

Common cuckoos have been seen flying in a recognizably hawklike fashion, flapping and gliding in a soaring flight very much like a bird of prey. When they settle, they are sometimes mobbed by meadow pipits, *Anthus pratensis*, and by other small birds. On a few occasions this behavior has been followed by the cuckoo alighting near a meadow pipit's nest, and one has been observed flying away with a pipit's egg, which it swallowed. It seems that the cuckoo indulges in this hawklike flight just before egg-laying to lure the owners of the nest away so that it can enter the nest and lay its own egg.

Evidence for this hypothesis is not conclusive but similar behavior has been seen in other cuckoos. The Indian hawk-cuckoo, *Cuculus varius*, which imitates sparrow hawks, has been seen to lure birds from their nests. The koel, *Eudynamys scolopacea*, mimics a crow, which is its main host in India. The male koel is black and it flies up to the host nest, calling, only to be promptly chased away by the crows. Apparently the crows act in this way not so much to ward off a parasitic bird but to assert their ownership of the nest, in the same way that they would if it was threatened by another crow. While the male koel is being chased away by the nest's owners, the brown female koel slips in to lay her egg. The young koel does not eject its nestmates. In appearance it is hardly distinguishable from its fellow nestlings and is readily accepted by parents and siblings.

The young cuckoo monopolizes the host parents' attentions long after it has outgrown their nest. It does so by employing tactics such as imitating the begging calls of the hosts' natural offspring and by using the visual impact of its widely gaping mouth.

CUCKOO-SHRIKE

ALTHOUGH THE CUCKOO-SHRIKES look like both cuckoos and shrikes, they are related to neither. DNA analysis suggests that they are more closely related to the orioles of Africa, Asia, the Philippines, New Guinea and Australia. The geographical distribution of cuckoo-shrikes is very similar to that of the Old World orioles.

Many cuckoo-shrikes have a shrike-like hooked bill and cuckoolike, black and white barred plumage on their underparts. In general, the plumage is a dull combination of gray, black and white, though some species have more striking coloration. The male red-shouldered cuckoo-shrike, *Campephaga phoenicea*, has a patch of red on each wing but is otherwise black. The barred cuckoo-shrike, *Coracina lineata*, looks very much like the common cuckoo of Eurasia, with a gray head and neck as well as a barred breast. The 14-inch (36 cm) ground cuckoo-shrike, *Pteropodocys maxima*, has a similar appearance, and many cuckoo-shrikes have a cuckoolike flight. The plumage of the sexes differs in all species, the females being paler and less conspicuous than the males.

Some cuckoo-shrikes are commonly called graybirds, trillers, cicada birds or flycatcher shrikes. The minivets (*Pericrocotus* spp.) are in the cuckoo-shrike family but are distinct from the rest and are sometimes placed in a separate subfamily. Minivets are brightly colored birds and their plumage offers a marked contrast to the plainer colors of most cuckoo-shrikes.

Mixed parties

Some cuckoo-shrikes migrate, especially in Australia, where they move from the south of the continent to the warmer northern parts in winter. The black-faced cuckoo-shrike, *Coracina novaehollandiae*, occasionally strays to New Zealand. In Australia it is called the blue jay or shufflewing. The latter name is derived from the way it shuffles and restows its wings when it alights.

Outside the breeding season many cuckoo-shrikes live in flocks, often mixed with other birds. For instance, the black-and-white triller, *Lalage melanoleuca*, of the Philippines, associates with woodpeckers and orioles. Nearly all the cuckoo-shrikes live among trees, favoring forest edges, gardens and coastal vegetation, and rarely come down to the ground. One exception is the ground cuckoo-shrike of Australia, which lives in flocks on treeless plains outside the breeding season. It is able to move swiftly across the ground, unlike other cuckoo-shrikes. Each flock is made up of a family, parents and offspring, that stays together from the time the chicks leave the nest until the next breeding season.

The "caterpillar birds"

The scientific name Campephagidae, meaning caterpillar-eaters, describes the birds in this family more appropriately than the name cuckoo-shrike. Some cuckoo-shrikes, such as the white-winged triller, *L. sueurii*, eat caterpillars that damage crops. Sometimes such cuckoo-shrikes are called caterpillar-shrikes; another group are called cicada birds because of the large numbers of cicadas they eat. Cuckoo-shrikes eat a wide variety of other insects, however, including grasshoppers, bugs and beetles. The black-breasted triller, *Chlamydochaera jefferyi*, is unusual because it feeds mainly on fruit.

Some of the smaller cuckoo-shrike species, such as the pygmy triller or pied shrike, *Hemipus picatus*, hunt in the manner of flycatchers, flying out from a perch and returning after catching flying ants and other insects on the wing. Others hunt insects living on leaves and twigs. The pied triller, *L. nigra*, of Malaysia, and the black-faced cuckoo-shrike sometimes seize insects from the ground. The latter behaves like a shrike in seeking out food, watching from a favorite perch and then swooping down to catch an insect, worm or other invertebrate.

Cuckoo-shrike nests are usually placed high up in the branches of a tree. This is the black-faced cuckoo-shrike of Australasia and parts of Southeast Asia.

Frail nests

Cuckoo-shrike nests are built high up in trees. The ground cuckoo-shrike builds in branches 30 feet (9 m) or so high. Its small nest is made of grasses, flower stems, creepers and other soft vegetation bound together with cobwebs, and is relatively fragile. The nest of the white-winged triller is built with a rim 1 inch (2.5 cm) high but becomes gradually flattened by the parents repeatedly landing on it. By the end of the season only a flat platform is left.

In most species of cuckoo-shrikes the female does most of the nest-building with the male acting as the onlooker. In some species only the female incubates the eggs, though sometimes the male shares this task, or stands over the eggs with his wings half opened to protect them from the sun. The ground cuckoo-shrike family stays together for the rest of the year, and before the families leave the breeding grounds, where the nests are close to each other, the young birds are fed indiscriminately by any adults, not necessarily just their own parents.

Both sexes of the white-winged triller participate in building the nest. Having achieved this task and carried out his share of the incubation, the male feeds the chicks during their first week. After this he spends most of his time singing.

The female African white-breasted cuckoo-shrike, *Coracina pectoralis*, usually builds the nest on her own, although the male sometimes performs this duty himself. He gathers only one tiny piece of material, perhaps a fine twig or a blade of grass, on each collecting trip. Observation of one male revealed that he took 4 minutes on average to collect a piece of material and add it to the nest. The nest took 6 days to complete. His mate did not contribute to the construction of the nest except to test each piece of material as it was fastened in place.

Threatened cuckoo-shrikes

Most cuckoo-shrikes are relatively common and not under threat. However, the populations of some species are thought to be decreasing locally. Widespread forest clearance on the island of Guimaras in the Philippines is believed to have caused the white-winged cuckoo-shrike, *Coracina ostenta*, to have become extinct there. The Réunion cuckoo-shrike, *C. newtoni*, endemic to Réunion Island, is restricted to two small, unprotected areas in the northwest of the island. Forestry activities and the introduction of deer have degraded its habitat. The black-bibbed cicada bird, *Coracina mindanensis*, which is endemic to several islands in the Philippines, has also suffered from habitat degradation and several races (subspecies) of this species are now thought to be uncommon or extremely rare.

RED-SHOULDERED CUCKOO-SHRIKE

CLASS	**Aves**
ORDER	**Passeriformes**
FAMILY	**Campephagidae**
GENUS AND SPECIES	***Campephaga phoenicea***

ALTERNATIVE NAME
Black cuckoo-shrike

WEIGHT
About 1 oz. (27 g)

LENGTH
Head to tail: 8¼–8⅔ in. (21–22 cm); wingspan: 7½–8 in. (19–20 cm)

DISTINCTIVE FEATURES
Broad-based, slightly hooked bill. Male: glossy black plumage; orange-red patch on shoulder. Female: grayish upperparts; black wing coverts fringed with yellow; whitish underparts with noticeable gray barring.

DIET
Insects, especially larvae

BREEDING
Age at first breeding: 1 year; breeding season: March–December, varies according to region; number of eggs: 2; incubation period: not known; fledging period: not known; breeding interval: 1 year

LIFE SPAN
Not known

HABITAT
Gardens, forest margins, wooded grassland, thickets in savanna, coastal vegetation

DISTRIBUTION
Senegal and the Gambia east to Uganda, western Kenya and Ethiopia

STATUS
Locally common in breeding range

Red-shouldered cuckoo-shrike

CURASSOW

THERE ARE 14 SPECIES of curassow, belonging to the same order as the chickens, pheasants and quails. They range from the size of a pheasant to that of a small turkey, the largest species being the great curassow, *Crax rubra*, which weighs up to about 10½ pounds (4.8 kg). The male's plumage is usually dark brown or black, sometimes flecked with white and glossed with dark green. The females of some species have a similar color to the males; others are more brown. Curassows have long tails and long legs and their most distinctive features are usually their crests and horny casques, or helmets.

The name curassow is derived from the island of Curaçao in the Caribbean, although curassows have never lived there. The Trinidad white-headed curassow, *Pipile pipile*, lives in Trinidad and Tobago but is not considered a true curassow. In fact, curassows are restricted to the American mainland, from Mexico south to northern Argentina and Uruguay.

Birds with helmets

Curassows are native to the forests of Central and South America. They have a variety of remarkable crests and casques, similar in shape to the helmets of Roman soldiers. The crests are formed by a double row of short, stiff feathers that curl forward in the great curassow and black curassow, *C. alector*. The casques are bony, horn-covered projections rising from the top of the bill. The casque of the razor-billed curassow, *Mitu mitu*, is scarlet and that of the helmeted curassow, *Pauxi pauxi*, is blue. The latter grows 1–3 inches (2.5–7.5 cm) high, covering the crown of the head. Those curassows without a crest generally have wattles or a fleshy knob of red or yellow at the base of the bill, which swells and brightens in the breeding season.

Forest residents

Curassows generally live deep in forests or on the forest margins although some species are known to visit open brush country. Unlike many of their gamebird relatives, curassows are not confined to the ground and spend a significant amount of time in trees. The great curassow runs about the forest floor in the manner of a turkey. If frightened it clambers into trees, half flying and half hopping until it can launch itself from a treetop and glide away to safety on its short, rounded wings.

Curassows feed on fruits, nuts, buds and fresh leaves. Occasionally they also take insects and small frogs. Young curassows seem to feed mostly on insects. Apart from the mainly ground-living great curassow the birds tend to feed in the frees. However, they also feed on fallen fruit and scratch through the litter on the forest floor.

Most male curassows have a far-carrying, bellowing call. However, the male yellow-knobbed curassow, Crax daubentoni, *produces a prolonged, high-pitched whistle.*

Tree nesters

Curassows are the only members of their order of gamebirds that nest in trees. Other Galliformes rear their young on the ground. At the start of the breeding season male curassows take up territories and show off to rival males and prospective mates by calling from the tops of trees. Curassows have a looped trachea (windpipe) that serves to amplify their calls. Their muffled bellows can be heard for some distance across the forest.

The male curassow courts the female by strutting before her with tail raised and head held high. The breast is tilted low and wings droop to display the white feathers under them. The sharing of parental duties varies between species. The male great curassow builds the nest alone but his mate feeds the chicks. In other species both sexes contribute to nest building, incubation of the eggs and feeding of the chicks.

The nest is built of twigs and lined with green leaves, which are sometimes replaced when they dry out. It is small compared to the

The razor-billed curassow is known as mutum *by Brazilians. Its brilliant red bill is a characteristic shared by several species of curassows.*

GREAT CURASSOW

CLASS	**Aves**
ORDER	**Galliformes**
FAMILY	**Cracidae**
GENUS AND SPECIES	***Crax rubra***

ALTERNATIVE NAMES
Mexican curassow; great crested curassow; globose curassow

WEIGHT
Up to 10½ lb. (4.8 kg)

LENGTH
Head to tail: 30–36 in. (75–90 cm)

DISTINCTIVE FEATURES
Large size; long neck, legs and tail. Male: mainly black plumage except for white belly; black crest; yellow knob on black bill. Female: 3 morphs (plumage varieties): barred, red and dark.

DIET
Mainly fallen fruit; occasionally fruits on trees

BREEDING
Age at first breeding: probably 2 years; breeding season: eggs laid February–May; number of eggs: 2; incubation period: about 32 days; fledging period: 4–5 days; breeding interval: 1 year

LIFE SPAN
Up to 24 years in captivity

HABITAT
Tropical and subtropical rain forest, usually in lowlands up to 4,000 ft. (1,200 m)

DISTRIBUTION
Eastern Mexico south to Ecuador

STATUS
Population not known, though not globally threatened

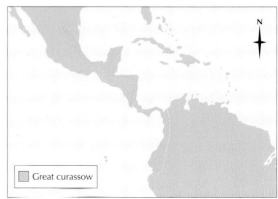

Great curassow

size of the curassow and so loosely woven that it is possible to see the large, rough-shelled eggs from underneath. Incubation lasts about a month and the young hatch with their wing feathers already well-developed. They leave the nest and walk among the branches on their first day. Within 4 or 5 days they can fly confidently, but according to some accounts, the young of the great curassow throw themselves from the nest to the ground before they can fly.

At first the curassow chicks are fed mainly on insects by their parents, but they soon learn to forage for themselves. The family often remains together for the rest of the year. Groups of curassows larger than one family are usually seen only where they have gathered at a large crop of fruit. Living in the trees, curassows fall prey to tree-living carnivores such as kinkajous and jaguars.

Difficult to breed

Europeans first encountered curassows in the villages of Central and South America. The local inhabitants reared them for the pot, having taken the eggs from the curassows' nests and hand-reared the chicks. Chickens, pheasants, turkeys and quails had all been successfully domesticated and early Spanish explorers regarded curassows as birds that could potentially be bred to produce quantities of flavorsome flesh. But the Spaniards found it impossible to breed them. The curassow is a bird of tropical forests and thickets, and requires warmth and seclusion. Moreover, it

lives in trees rather than on the ground, and it requires plenty of perching space in order for it to remain healthy. Knowledge of these factors has since allowed curassows to be successfully bred in zoos in the United States and Europe.

Conservation

Habitat destruction and overhunting are the greatest threats to the survival of the curassows. Curassow meat tastes like turkey, though it has a richer flavor, and both birds are plump-bodied. Even if curassows were tasteless, the amount of meat on them would make the birds a favorite target for hunters.

Many curassow species are threatened. Deforestation and hunting have resulted in a decline in the numbers of the blue-billed curassow, *Crax alberti*. The species now inhabits only a restricted range in northern Colombia. The red-billed curassow, *C. blumenbachii*, which was once found throughout the lowland Atlantic forest in southeast Brazil, is now limited to five protected areas of forest. Several of these are known to be subject to poaching. In the late 20th century one subspecies of the razor-billed curassow, *Mitu mitu mitu*, was rediscovered in forest in Alagoas, northeastern Brazil, after 300 years. However, due to hunting and habitat loss it is now believed to be extinct in the wild. A private captive population, numbering 11 individuals in 1984, may provide the subspecies with its only remaining hope of survival.

The Amazonian razor-billed curassow, Mitu mitu tuberosa, is common within its range. However, other subspecies of this curassow are severely threatened by hunting and habitat destruction.

CURLEW

Curlews typically build their nests in grass-filled hollows among low vegetation. Both parents incubate the eggs.

THE CURLEWS ARE THE LARGEST members of the family Scolopacidae and are distinguished by their long, curved bills. They derive their name from the two-syllable fluting call of the species that is commonly heard across much of northern and western Europe.

Altogether there are eight birds belonging to the curlew genus. The common or Eurasian curlew, *Numenius argquata*, is one of the larger species. It has streaky brown plumage, a white rump and a characteristic 4–6-inch (10–15-cm) decurved bill. The whimbrel, or Hudsonian curlew, *N. phaeopus*, is similar in appearance to the Eurasian curlew, though it is smaller and less shy. Other curlews are similar to the whimbrel in size and plumage, with the exception of the long-billed curlew, *N. americanus*, and the Madagascar curlew, *N. madagascariensis*, both of which are slightly larger than the Eurasian curlew.

The breeding range of the Eurasian curlew extends from the British Isles across Europe and Asia to China. The whimbrel has a discontinuous breeding range that includes Alaska, the west coast of Hudson Bay, Iceland, Scandinavia, northern European Russia and eastern Siberia.

The long-billed curlew is the North American counterpart of the Eurasian curlew and once bred over most of North America before farming diminished its range.

Curlews occur in Africa only as migrants, the Eurasian curlew moving as far south as South Africa in the northern winter. The name Madagascar curlew is a misnomer. This bird breeds in eastern Siberia and migrates to Malaysia and Australia. Its name comes from the Macassar Straits near the Sulawesi Archipelago, where the first specimen was collected.

Cosmopolitan migrants

Curlews are birds of open country, such as prairies, steppes, moors and marshes, where they gather in large flocks that may number several hundred in winter or on migration. Most species of curlew undertake long migrations. The bristle-thighed curlew, *N. tahitiensis*, named for the vaneless feathers on the thighs, breeds in Alaska and western Canada, but migrates 5,000 miles (8,000 km) to winter on islands in the Pacific. Some Eurasian curlews turn up on the east coast of North America in fall and winter.

EURASIAN CURLEW

CLASS **Aves**

ORDER **Charadriiformes**

FAMILY **Scolopacidae**

GENUS AND SPECIES *Numenius arquata*

ALTERNATIVE NAMES
Common curlew; western curlew; European curlew

LENGTH
Head to tail: 19½–24 in. (50–60 cm); wingspan: 31½–39 in. (80–100 cm)

DISTINCTIVE FEATURES
Very long, decurved bill; long legs; brownish plumage with pattern of brown and buff streaks; white rump (visible in flight only)

DIET
Mainly invertebrates, especially marine worms and crustaceans; some berries and seeds; rarely small fish and frogs

BREEDING
Age at first breeding: 2 years; breeding season: late April–August; number of eggs: 4; incubation period: 27–29 days; fledging period: 32–38 days; breeding interval: 1 year

LIFE SPAN
Up to 30 years, usually much less

HABITAT
Breeds on damp moors and tundra. Winters in coastal habitats, especially muddy estuaries and salt marshes.

DISTRIBUTION
Breeds in northern and central Europe and Siberia. Winters along coasts of northwestern Europe, Mediterranean, Africa, the Middle East and southern Asia.

STATUS
Common

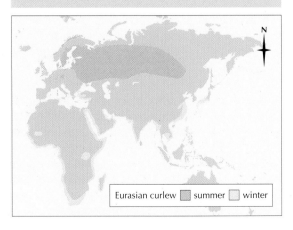

Eurasian curlew ▢ summer ▢ winter

Probing for food

Curlews feed on a variety of small animals, together with a few berries and seeds. Shellfish, crustaceans, insects, worms, small fish and frogs are all eaten, depending on season and locality. In the British Isles curlews search cattle fields for dung beetles from July to October, deserting them in November for stubble fields. Observations in Hungary revealed that Eurasian curlews and whimbrels feed on large numbers of agricultural pests such as owlet moth caterpillars, also known as army worms, and certain crickets. Indeed, scientists found that 96 percent of the whimbrel's food consisted of insects that are destructive to crops or vegetation. Shores, swamps and moors also provide sources of food. Curlews either pick their prey up from the surface of the ground or water or probe underground with their long bills for marine worms and deep-burrowing shellfish. The curlews pick up small animals in the tip of the bill and toss them into the mouth by jerks of the head.

The bristle-thighed curlew has the unusual habit, for a shorebird, of stealing eggs, especially those of seabirds. While in its Pacific island wintering grounds, this curlew steals the eggs of terns, boobies and frigate birds, impaling them on its bill and carrying them away to smash and eat at its leisure.

Nesting in the open

The male curlew defends his territory and advertises for a mate by singing while airborne. He flies low over the ground and then rises steeply

In the breeding season, curlews inhabit open country, such as moorland, tundra, steppes and prairies.

Curlews winter in coastal areas, favoring marshes and the intertidal zones of estuaries.

and hangs poised before drifting to the ground with wings outstretched, all the time pouring out his bubbling song.

Curlew nests are grass-lined hollows in low vegetation such as heather and are found on open moors and pastures and in woodland clearings. The female usually lays four eggs, which are incubated by both parents for about 4½–5½ weeks. The young are able to leave the nest shortly after hatching and creep away to hide when they are not feeding with their parents. The adult curlews defend their offspring vigorously, attacking harriers and crows, and even luring enemies away by feigning injury.

Curlews' changing fortunes

Vast flocks of Eskimo curlews, *N. borealis*, once migrated down the eastern seaboard of North America, having gorged themselves on the crowberries of Labrador and Newfoundland. They were known as doughbirds because, when shot, their breasts split open on hitting the ground to reveal soft, doughlike fat. In the 1950s they were thought to be extinct, and it seemed that another bird had gone the way of the passenger pigeon, *Ectopistes migratorius*. Both species had existed in huge numbers but had been exterminated due to overhunting. However, rumors of the extinction of the curlew were premature. In 1959 an Eskimo curlew was seen at Galveston Island, Texas, the

first sighting since 1945. Others have been seen since, and ornithologists presume that at least one group of Eskimo curlews is still breeding, although its whereabouts are not known. The population of this species has shown no significant increase since hunting was outlawed and scientists believe that there may be some significant ecological factor that prevents the Eskimo curlew population from recovering.

Bristle-thighed curlews are familiar in their winter haunts, and it is well-known that they migrated up to Alaska, but for many years no one knew where they bred. For some time this curlew remained the only bird in North America the nest of which had never been seen, but in 1948 two members of a National Geographic Society expedition camped near the Yukon River observed two bristle-thighed curlews repeatedly returning to one place. They approached cautiously, and after running forward, saw one of the birds fly from its well-concealed nest.

Other curlew species are also widely believed to be endangered. The slender-billed curlew, *N. tenuirostris*, which was common in the 19th century, is today thought to breed only in Russia. Estimates of its current population range from 50 to 270 birds. Ornithologists believe that overhunting and the drainage of the habitat used by the birds on migration, called passage habitat, are the main causes of the species' decline.

CUSCUS

CUSCUSES ARE UNUSUAL marsupials that are often mistaken for monkeys. They have a rounded head, small ears almost buried in their fur, protruding yellow- or red-rimmed eyes, a short muzzle and a yellow or pink nose. The color of cuscus fur varies from white, cream, buff and reddish to gray, grayish green and black. Cuscuses are similar in size to large domestic cats, growing to about 2¾ feet (85 cm) in length, including the long prehensile tail. It has been suggested that the name cuscus refers to the scolding or "cussing" sound that the animals sometimes make, but in fact it derives from *couscous*, the French rendering of the animals' aboriginal Papua New Guinea name. There are at least seven cuscus species living in the forests of Queensland, Australia, and the jungles of New Guinea.

The hind feet are useful for grasping branches, the long first toe being thumblike, opposable and particularly strong. All cuscuses have five toes; apart from the first digit, every other toe has a claw. The second and third toes are syndactylous (bound together by skin) and their claws are used, as in kangaroos, for combing the fur. Female cuscuses have a pouch in which the young develop.

Bouts of cussing

Cuscuses are arboreal (tree-dwelling) and are adept at clinging to branches with the hind feet and the prehensile tail, which can be wrapped around a branch for extra support when climbing. At rest, the tail is tightly coiled, a little like a watch spring.

Cuscuses live in thick cover, well hidden among foliage, and generally remain still during the day. Many cuscus species feed and nest alone. At night they move about among the trees feeding on fruits, flowers, leaves, insects and sometimes eggs and small birds. When feeding, cuscuses grip a branch with the hind feet and tail, leaving the front feet free to hold food. In captivity cuscuses eat fruit and vegetables.

When challenging an animal, or quarrelling with another cuscus, the usually gentle and inoffensive cuscus snarls and barks, in a guttural voice. As it begins to bark, it raises a forepaw in a menacing gesture and, if further provoked, strikes out with its front feet, perhaps even biting the other animal.

The spotted cuscus

The most familiar cuscus species is the spotted cuscus, *Spilocuscus maculatus*, which ranges from Queensland, northern Australia, to northern and eastern New Guinea. In New Guinea the male and female spotted cuscuses are so unlike that they were originally thought to belong to different species.

The female's fur may be gray, brown or fawn; it is a little lighter on the sides of the head but is generally more uniform than that of the male. A patch of fur on the animal's rump, found in all cuscuses whatever the species or sex, is also pale. As the female gets older, this patch becomes lighter still. This is because the fur is worn down in this area due to the animal's habit of sitting so regularly in one position throughout the day.

In contrast with the female, the male spotted cuscus in New Guinea is creamy white when young. At first the male's coat is covered with uniformly spaced spots of approximately ½ inch (1.3 cm) in diameter. These spots are generally dark in color. As the animal grows older, the

The spotted cuscus's patterning provides the animal with effective camouflage against the sun-dappled branches of its native habitat.

CUSCUSES

CLASS	**Mammalia**
ORDER	**Marsupialia**
FAMILY	**Phalangeridae**
GENUS	***Spilocuscus*** and ***Phalanger***
SPECIES	**About 10, including spotted cuscus, *S. maculatus*; and gray cuscus, *P. mimilus***

WEIGHT
***S. maculatus*: 6½–9 lb. (3–4 kg)**

LENGTH
Head and body: 13–17 in. (34–43 cm); tail: 12–17 in. (30–43 cm)

DISTINCTIVE FEATURES
Rounded head; large eyes; thick fur; long, prehensile tail; opposable digit on hind foot; considerable color variation between species, ranging from white, cream and reddish to dark gray and black; different patterning for male and female

DIET
Fruits, flowers, vegetation and insects; sometimes eggs and small birds

BREEDING
Breeding season: probably all year; number of young: usually 1

HABITAT
Tropical rain forest from mountains to lowlands; also mangrove swamps

DISTRIBUTION
New Guinea and northeastern Australia

STATUS
Several species endangered or vulnerable: Woodlark Island cuscus, *P. lullulae*; black-spotted cuscus, *S. rufoniger*; obi cuscus, *P. rothschildi*; southern common cuscus, *P. intercastellanus*; and silky cuscus, *P. sericeus*

A cuscus's tail may be as long as its body. Combined with the strong toes on the hind feet, the powerful prehensile tail enables the cuscus to maintain a sure grip when tree climbing.

spots grow and run into each other, forming irregular blotches. Consequently, the male becomes darker and more uniform with age.

An endangered group

Several cuscus species native to eastern New Guinea are rare, but the Woodlark Island cuscus, *Phalanger lullulae*, is believed to be one of the most highly endangered. Only eight specimens have ever been seen. The last four were taken in 1953 and it is not known whether any have been seen since. Development of the land on Woodlark Island for agriculture and commercial logging is believed to have dramatically reduced the available natural habitat of the species. Many environmental groups argue that safe habitat must be set aside if the species is to survive.

The black-spotted cuscus, *S. rufoniger*, which is native to the rain forests of north and east New Guinea, is also believed to be endangered. Its numbers have declined dramatically over recent years. At 13–15 pounds (6–7 kg) the black-spotted cuscus is heavier than many cuscus species and is more conspicuous than most. Although it is of little economic value to humans, its size makes it an easy target for hunters who kill the animal for its coat and meat.

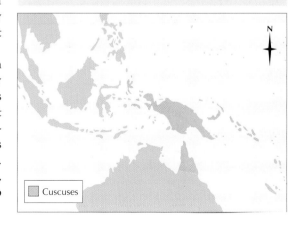

Cuscuses

CUTTLEFISH

THE CUTTLEFISH ARE MOLLUSKS belonging to the subclass Coleoidea and are related to octopuses and squids. The body is shield-shaped, the margins forming two thin, narrow fins. The relatively small head bears eight arms. There are two long tentacles, which are retracted into a pocket beside each eye at rest. The arms are then held together forming a cone with the apex directed forward. Suckers sprout from each arm and also from the club-shaped ends of the tentacles. Each sucker is on a short muscular stalk and its rim is strengthened by a horny flange with a serrated edge. The shell is internal. It is almost as long as the body and has a horny margin. Its chalky center is honeycombed with gas-filled chambers, which help to keep the cuttlefish buoyant in the water. In common with other coleoids, the cuttlefish has a much larger and more developed brain than other mollusks.

Widespread in shallow waters

There are about 100 species of cuttlefish. Most live in tropical and subtropical seas, mainly in shallow waters, though a few are deep-sea species. The best known species, the common cuttlefish, was first described in detail by Aristotle over 2,000 years ago. It ranges over the eastern North Atlantic, as far north as the North

Pigment-containing structures known as chromatophores are embedded in the skin of cuttlefish (common cuttlefish, below). These enable them to adopt a wide range of colors and patterns.

The harvest cuttlefish occurs in Australian waters. Cuttlefish adopt vibrant colors for different reasons. Rapid, dramatic color changes probably scare away predators and form part of courtship.

Sea and south to the coast of southern Africa. It also occurs in the Mediterranean. Including its tentacles, the common cuttlefish may grow up to 31 inches (80 cm) long, approximately 15 inches (40 cm) of which is the body length. The smallest known species of cuttlefish is 1½ inches (4 cm) overall, while the largest species reach as much as 5 feet (1.5 m).

Jet-propelled mollusks

The common cuttlefish's ground color is creamy gray, but it uses bags of pigment (chromatophores) embedded in its skin to change color. These are highly elastic and can be contracted or expanded by the use of muscle fibers. The pigments are mainly yellow, orange, brown, red and black, and a combination of these can produce a wide range of colors. A cuttlefish swimming over a rock covered with weeds and sedentary animals of various colors will change from gray to reddish brown and back again, to light brown or greenish, as it passes over the corresponding patches of color.

Cuttlefish can change color in less than a second, and some scientists believe that they are capable of more significant and rapid color changes than any other animals. Cuttlefish swim in shoals, moving and changing color in unison. A change in color may be brought about for various reasons. It offers the cuttlefish a means of camouflage, but it may also alarm potential predators and form part of courtship rituals.

To breathe, the cuttlefish draws water over its gills, which remove the oxygen. The water then passes through the anus and the kidney openings, finally being expelled as a jet through the funnel. This can eject a stream of water with force, driving the animal through the water using

a form of jet propulsion. The funnel can be turned in any direction, and the cuttlefish moves in the opposite direction to that in which the water is expelled. The cuttlefish also uses its funnel to maintain its position in the water. A cuttlefish that appears to be quite stationary just

COMMON CUTTLEFISH

PHYLUM **Mollusca**

CLASS **Cephalopoda**

ORDER **Sepioidea**

FAMILY **Sepiidae**

GENUS AND SPECIES *Sepia officinalis*

ALTERNATIVE NAME
Common cuttle

LENGTH
Overall (including arms and tentacles): up to 31 in. (80 cm); body: up to 15 in. (40 cm)

DISTINCTIVE FEATURES
Shield-shaped body with marginal fins; 8 arms lined with suckers; 2 long tentacles; changes color to match surroundings

DIET
Mainly fish and small crustaceans

BREEDING
Breeding season: spring and summer; number of eggs: up to 300; hatching period: about 60 days

LIFE SPAN
Usually 1–2 years

HABITAT
Shallow waters under 820 ft. (250 m) deep

DISTRIBUTION
East Atlantic coastlines from Norway south to southern Africa; also in Mediterranean

STATUS
Common

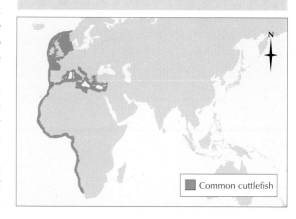

Common cuttlefish

beneath the surface of the water can be seen constantly turning its funnel first in one direction, then in another, giving a brief puff each time. Combined with an undulation of the fins, the effect of these gentle jets is to keep the cuttlefish in one spot. The animal can also pivot on its own axis by making the fin on one side work in the reverse direction to the other, at the same time using the funnel to drive itself around.

The funnel is also used to eject a blue-black, inklike substance. All coleoids have a tubular outgrowth known as a diverticulum in the intestine. Also called the ink sac, the diverticulum is filled with a blue-black liquid. When the coleoid senses danger, the liquid is emptied first into its intestine and then into its mantle cavity, from where it is expelled into the water. The ink enables the cuttlefish to conceal itself from a predator and confuses the attacker's sense of smell. Cuttlefish can quickly replenish their supply of the liquid and consequently can issue repeated ejections if necessary, enough to color about 700 cubic feet (20 cu. m) of water in only a few minutes. Even tiny cuttlefish, just hatched, will eject ink if disturbed.

Hunting with tentacles

A cuttlefish feeds by day on shrimps, prawns, crabs and fish. Stalking its prey until it is within range, the cuttlefish rapidly extends its two tentacles and uses them to bring food back to the mouth, which is armed with a horny, parrotlike beak and a filelike tongue, or radula.

Cuttlefish seize crabs from behind, and drop them if they bring their claws into play. They also take large dead fish, tearing them open with the beak before inserting the tonglike tentacles to remove pieces of flesh. Cuttlefish flush shrimps from the sand by disturbing them with jets from the funnel on the underside of the body. As the shrimps are exposed, the cuttlefish grab them using their tentacles. The chief predators of cuttlefish are sharks, dolphins, porpoises and small whales.

Colorful courtship

Mating occurs in spring and summer and is accompanied by a dramatic show of color. The cuttlefish adopts a kind of zebra pattern, which is more brightly defined in males than in females. One of the arms on the left side of the male becomes modified during the courtship period. Some of the suckers near its base are lost and the arm, known as the hectocotylus, is used to transfer sperm to the female's funnel, which contains the reproductive organs. The females are often luminous during the mating period.

The eggs are laid singly, passing out through the female's funnel, where they are fertilized and coated with a latexlike solution that is colored with a squirt of ink. Each capsule formed by the hardening of the solution bears a long stalk. The stalks of the eggs are entwined on a support by the female; alternatively she may tangle stalks of a succession of eggs on each other to form clusters of capsules. These grapelike bunches sometimes come adrift. Each female lays up to 300 eggs in batches of 20 to 30.

When it hatches the young cuttlefish is about ½ inches (1.3 cm) long, and resembles the parent except for its proportionately larger head and eyes. It feeds on copepods (minute crustaceans).

In common with the squids, cuttlefish have eight arms, all of similar length, and two tentacles that grow far longer than the arms. Cuttlefish move by a form of jet propulsion.

DAB

Dabs have superb camouflage, a trait shared with other bottom-living flatfish such as the soles and flounders.

THE DAB IS A SMALL FLATFISH that lives in the shallow seas of the North Atlantic, including the Baltic Sea. It reaches a maximum length of 16 inches (40 cm), though 8 inches (20 cm) is a more usual size, and weighs approximately 2 pounds (1.3 kg). The fish may be recognized by the brownish color of the upper surface and by the shape of the lateral line, which is strongly curved opposite the pectoral fin. The dab's skin often features orange spots, similar to those on the plaice, *Pleuronectes platessa*, but smaller. The flattened body is fringed by the long dorsal and anal fins, the pectoral and pelvic fins being relatively reduced in size. The scales on the upper surface are toothed on the rear margin and rough to the touch. The undersurface of the dab is white and its scales have smooth margins.

Lies on sandy seabeds

The dab is a bottom-living fish and is found in enormous numbers in sandy bays. Shoals of dab include fish that are about 1 inch (2.5 cm) long that have recently completed their free-swimming life nearer the surface of the water and have settled on the bottom. The dab lives close inshore, particularly in September, when it is caught in large numbers in shrimp trawls and push nets. Its habits are similar to those of the plaice, and the two species frequently compete for food. However, as the dab keeps to inshore waters for most of the year, whereas plaice tend to move offshore for part of the year, their mutual food supplies do not become exhausted.

Bottom-feeding fish

The dab has especially strong teeth in the lower jaw, which enable it to take a wider range of food than the plaice. It eats almost any small, bottom-living invertebrates, including starfish, crabs, mollusks and worms, as well as small fish. The dab feeds in a similar way to the lemon sole, *Microstomus kitt*, but strikes obliquely at its prey when launching an attack.

The dab is not an active fish. It spends long periods lying on the seabed. When moving over the sea bottom, it may use the long dorsal and anal fins fringing the body to get a grip to move forward slowly, or it may, by undulating these, progress at a fair speed. Indeed, when disturbed, a dab can use its tail to shoot through the water, just above the sea bottom, with considerable speed.

Dramatic transformation

The dab that inhabit the western part of the English Channel breed from February to April; those in the northern North Sea breed between April and June. Each female lays 80,000 to 130,000 eggs, each 0.6–1.2 millimeters in diameter. These float at the surface and hatch in 3–12 days, according to the temperature. The embryo develops more quickly in warmer water.

Each egg is well supplied with yolk and the newly hatched fish, then 0.25 millimeters long, carries on its underside the remains of the yolk sac. Mouth, jaws and digestive tract are not developed for a further 10–11 days, during which time the young dabs use up the yolk.

The young dab at first looks like the young of any other fish. Its body is rounded, its fins grow from the conventional places and it has an eye on either side of its head. But its jaws soon start to become twisted, metamorphosing by ⅔ inches (1.5 cm). During the next 2–4 months further striking transformations take place in the fish's shape. The dorsal and anal fins in other fish

DAB

CLASS	**Osteichthyes**
ORDER	**Pleuronectiformes**
FAMILY	**Pleuronectidae**
GENUS AND SPECIES	*Limanda limanda*

LENGTH
Usually about 8 in. (20 cm)

DISTINCTIVE FEATURES
Flattened body, fringed by long dorsal and anal fins; lateral line curved over pectoral fin; eyes on same side of head; upper side yellowish brown, often with indistinct blotches and spots; underside white

DIET
Crabs, mollusks, starfish, brittle stars and other bottom-living invertebrates; small fish

BREEDING
Age at first breeding: 2 years (male), 3 years (female); breeding season: February–June; number of eggs: tens of thousands; hatching period: 6–15 days at 39–50° F (4–10° C)

LIFE SPAN
Up to 12 years

HABITAT
Sandy shoals and banks at up to 490 ft. (150 m) deep; young only in shallows

DISTRIBUTION
North Atlantic, from southern Greenland to Newfoundland and from White Sea (Arctic waters to north of European Russia) to Spain

STATUS
Common, sometimes abundant

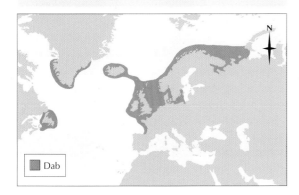

□ Dab

are relatively small and serve mainly as balancers. In the dab and related flatfish, they become very long, running down either side of the body, and acting as the main organs for swimming. At the same time that the dorsal and anal fins are enlarging, the body of the dab becomes flattened from side to side and the fish lies on one side. What was formerly the right side becomes the upper surface and the left side becomes the lower surface.

The most dramatic change in the young dab's form is provided by the left eye, which migrates around the head to lie alongside the right eye. In the mature dab, instead of an eye on either side of the body, there are two eyes near each other looking upward. In addition, a thick, dark lobe forms over each eye, covering the upper part of the pupil and shielding it from the light coming from above.

Flattened fish

The term flatfish is also applied to the skates and rays, related to sharks, in which a much simpler type of flattening occurs, from above downward. In the dab and in its relatives such as the soles and flounders, which are all bony fish, the bodies are flattened from side to side. The end result is much the same: a fish develops that is adapted to living and feeding on the seabed. In the skates and rays, this end is achieved with relatively little anatomical modification. In the flatfish proper, as represented by the dab, there are far more dramatic changes: the flattening and twisting that the fish undergo means that many parts of the body, the eyes and the jaws in particular, undergo radical modification.

One of the most interesting steps in this series of changes in the dab has to do with the migration of the left eye. Although the mature skull, like the rest of the skeleton, is made of bone, it begins as softer cartilage. In the newly hatched dab there is a bar of cartilage above each eye. Very soon after this the cartilage above the left eye is absorbed, so the eye can travel over the top of the head and on to the right side.

Young dabs have an eye on each side of the head, but as they grow the left eye migrates over the head to join the right one. Adults are thus asymmetrical in form. Pictured is an adult sand dab of the genus Citharichthys.

DADDY LONGLEGS

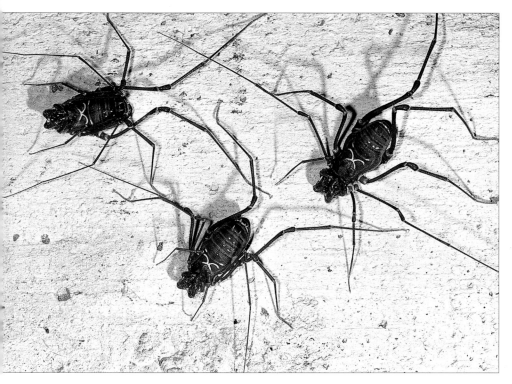

Unlike spiders, daddy longlegs do not have a clearly marked division between thorax and abdomen. They are further distinguished from spiders in that they do not produce venom or silk.

THREE DIFFERENT GROUPS of animals are commonly known as daddy longlegs. Adult crane flies, which are true flies of the order Diptera and family Tipulidae, are called daddy longlegs, particularly in Britain. Tipulids look like large mosquitoes, though they cannot bite. Like most insects, crane flies have three body parts (the head, thorax and abdomen) and, like most flies, they have only two wings. Cellar spiders are also known as daddy longlegs spiders. These are true spiders of the order Araneae and family Pholcidae. The third group of animals referred to as daddy longlegs are the members of the order Opiliones, although several species in this order have short legs. It is this final group that is discussed here.

Opiliones differ from true spiders in several important respects. They have only two eyes, positioned back to back on turrets on the thorax, whereas spiders have at least eight eyes arranged in a group on the head. In addition, while all true spiders have the abdomen sharply marked off from the thorax, daddy longlegs have no such waist. Unlike spiders, daddy longlegs never spin webs, as they do not produce silk. They do not produce venom either, although they do emit a foul-smelling odor when disturbed.

In general, male and female daddy longlegs are difficult to tell apart, although the male usually has longer legs and a smaller body than the female. In some species however, notably in the common *Phalangium opilio*, the pedi-palps (mouthparts) of the male are long, creating the impression that they are another pair of legs. The 7,000 species of daddy longlegs are distributed all over the world except for the polar regions. Only 23 species are found in Britain.

Losing valuable legs

Mainly inconspicuous in appearance, daddy longlegs are nevertheless familiar to most people. They live in woods and among long grass and other low-growing vegetation but, being largely nocturnal, they are more often seen beneath windowsills or when flowerpots are moved.

If it is disturbed, a daddy longlegs usually attempts to scuttle away on its long, threadlike legs. Sometimes one of the legs is lost as the insect makes its escape. The leg is thrown off at a breaking point between the first two joints. After coming away, the leg may twitch and quiver for some seconds. Daddy longlegs appear to suffer little inconvenience from the loss, although they cannot regenerate a lost limb. This fact further distinguishes them from true spiders, which are able to regrow all of their legs at once if need be. Daddy longlegs have been found still mobile with only two legs. The second pair of legs, usually the longest, carries sense organs. It is used to feel for obstacles and is held in the air to detect vibrations. These legs also seem to provide a sense of taste or smell. Loss of this pair of legs slows a daddy longlegs down considerably.

Eat almost anything

Daddy longlegs are omnivorous. They feed on a variety of small invertebrates, including insects, spiders and mites. However, they do not inject venom into their victims, as spiders do. Instead, they have large and powerful bill-like jaws, or chelicerae, with which to pierce the prey and suck out its juices and soft tissues. They also eat some of the more juicy forms of plant life. In captivity, daddy longlegs can be fed on almost anything edible, from bread and milk to meat; this is probably the reason why they are so common in garden garbage heaps. If a bottle containing scraps of meat and fat is placed with its opening level with the soil and left overnight, it will often contain one or more daddy longlegs in the morning. Daddy longlegs also need to drink at frequent intervals to keep themselves in

DADDY LONGLEGS

PHYLUM	**Arthropoda**
CLASS	**Arachnida**
ORDER	**Opiliones**
FAMILY	**Nemastomatidae, Phalangiidae and Trogulidae**
GENUS AND SPECIES	**7,000 species**

ALTERNATIVE NAMES
Harvest spider; harvester; harvestman

LENGTH
¾–3½ in. (2–9 cm)

DISTINCTIVE FEATURES
Superficially resemble spiders; body oval and undivided; 8 pairs of legs, long in most species; second pair of legs usually longest; 2 eyes on turrets; lack fangs, venom and silk

DIET
Mainly small insects, spiders and mites; also fruits, plant stems, carrion and detritus

BREEDING
Breeding season: summer (temperate regions), all year (Tropics); hatching period: several days or weeks

LIFE SPAN
Up to 1 year

HABITAT
Most species in cool, moist habitats

DISTRIBUTION
Worldwide, except polar regions

STATUS
Generally abundant or common; some species threatened, including all cave-dwelling species in Brazil

legs being hatched the following year. In others, the eggs hatch fairly quickly but the young hibernate through the winter. Apart from size, there is little or no difference between adult and young daddy longlegs. In some species, males are very rare and reproduction is largely by parthenogenesis (reproduction without mating, resulting in clones of the mother). This is especially true of *Megabunus diadema*, a species found on mountains in Britain. One count showed a ratio of only one male to more than 400 females.

Daddy longlegs grow by ecdysis, or molting, the whole skin being shed. There may be seven or eight such skin changes during a daddy longlegs' lifetime, with about 10 days between each. The molts usually take place at night. The gossamer-light sloughs, complete in every detail and intact down to the thinnest portions of each leg, may sometimes be found attached to low-growing vegetation to which the daddy longlegs usually anchors itself for the molt. The old skin splits and the body is drawn out from it. Then each long leg must be removed from its old casing. The daddy longlegs uses its jaws for this.

The legs of a daddy longlegs may grow up to 12 times its body length. They can be voluntarily amputated in emergencies, a process known as autonomy, but they will not grow back.

Anesthetic defense measure
Daddy longlegs are preyed on by centipedes and the larger spiders, as well as being taken by insectivorous birds. Their major defense is to cast off a limb, which may twitch and wriggle like a living thing, thereby attracting the attention of the predator long enough for the daddy longlegs to make good their escape.

The only other defense mechanism that daddy longlegs have is to discharge a foul-smelling, volatile fluid from glands near the eyes. This fluid seems to affect even daddy longlegs themselves if a group of them are placed in a closed container. They seem to be anesthetized by it, but quickly recover if they are taken out and exposed once more to the air.

good condition. They cannot endure long periods of starvation, unlike spiders, and lack of drinking water soon makes them stiff and torpid. A drink, however, quickly restores them.

Mating and molting
Daddy longlegs mate by internal fertilization and there is no courtship. Matings are frequent, the same male mating several times in rapid succession with the same partner or with other females. The female lays her eggs using an ovipositor. These are less than 5 millimeters in diameter and are laid in the soil and in crevices in the bark of trees, usually in late summer or fall. In some species, the eggs overwinter, young daddy long-

DAMSELFISH

Most damselfish, or demoiselles, live in shallow tropical waters, and particularly favor the area around coral reefs. Many species, such as the orange-colored garibaldi, *Hypsypops rubicunda*, and the blue chromis, *Chromis cyanea*, are brightly colored and some, such as the sergeant major, *Abudefduf saxatilis*, are spotted or striped. Most damselfish are less than 6 inches (15 cm) long. The body is deep and flattened from side to side, with prominent dorsal fins, the front one of which is spinous.

Quarrelsome demoiselles

Damselfish that live near coral reefs hover close to the coral heads, perhaps several hundred at a time. When disturbed, they dart with one accord into the crevices among the corals. Temperate species, such as the garibaldi of the Bay of California, live over kelp beds and on rocky coasts, places offering shelter equivalent to that of coral reefs. Many other damselfish species tend to inhabit the waters near large anemones and in several cases this has led to either a loose or a close symbiosis between the fish and the anemone. This reaches an extreme in the well-known association between the giant anemone and the small clownfish. As a result of the close relationship between certain damselfish and sea anemones, the former are sometimes referred to as anemonefish.

It is a feature of the damselfish family (Pomacentridae) that some species use their pectoral fins in an oarlike manner. The fins are brought forward almost edgewise and pulled back more or less broadside. Damselfish are often aggressive, with a strong territorial sense. Some live in pairs once they mature and are aggressive toward others of their kind that approach their particular shelters. As is common in fish, this strong territorial instinct is linked with a marked degree of parental care.

Damselfish communicate by making clicking noises with the pharyngeal teeth that line the throat. In recent studies scientists found that male domino damselfish, *Dascyllus albisella*, produced pulses of sound on specific occasions. These included courtship, the visit of a female, during mating, to show aggression toward heterospecifics (damselfish of another species) and conspecifics (damselfish of the same species) and when preparing a nest. The scientists found that females produced only aggressive sounds.

The coloration of damselfish is highly variable. Many species, such as the electric blue damsel, Pomacentrus coeruleus, are a striking shade of blue. Other species are red, yellow, orange or dramatically striped.

DAMSELFISH

CLASS **Osteichthyes**

ORDER **Perciformes**

FAMILY **Pomacentridae**

GENUS **28, including *Chromis*; *Abudefduf*; *Amphiprion*; *Premnas*; and *Hypsypops***

SPECIES **335, including blue chromis, *C. cyanea*; sergeant major, *Abudefduf saxatilis*; and anemonefish, *Amphiprion percula***

ALTERNATIVE NAMES
Demoiselle (all species); clownfish, anemonefish (*Amphiprion* and *Premnas* only)

WEIGHT
Up to 9 oz. (250 g)

LENGTH
Up to 13¾ in. (35 cm); most species 4–6 in. (10–15 cm)

DISTINCTIVE FEATURES
Oval or elongated, laterally compressed body; single dorsal fin; coloration generally bright, often with striking patterning

DIET
Varies with species. Diets include: algae; phytoplankton and zooplankton; other fish.

BREEDING
Varies according to species

LIFE SPAN
Up to 5 years

HABITAT
Most species: coral reefs; others: rocky seabeds and sea grass beds

DISTRIBUTION
Generally tropical and subtropical, coastal waters; also in Mediterranean

STATUS
Most species common. Vulnerable: *Chromis sanctaehelenae*, *Stegastes sanctaehelenae* and *S. sanctipauli*.

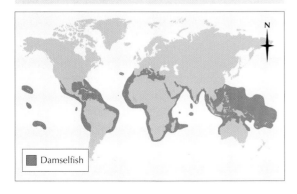

Damselfish

Some damselfish are herbivorous, feeding on algae and tending algal "gardens" in their territories. Other species feed on invertebrates or plankton while some are piscivorous, feeding mainly on smaller fish, even weaker individuals of their own kind, especially if there are not enough places in which the small fish may hide.

Prolific breeders

The scientist J. Garnaud studied breeding in the spotted damselfish of the tropical Indian and Pacific Oceans. Observing specimens in the aquarium at Monaco he found that each pair spawned in the early morning, as often as three times a month, and at each spawning the female laid 20,000 to 25,000 eggs. The eggs are sticky and are laid in small clusters, on rocks or other firm surfaces. The male guards the eggs until they hatch 4–5 days later. One species, *Acanthochromis polyacanthus*, also guards the larvae.

The garibaldi, another damselfish species studied by Garnaud, spawns at depths of 4–42 feet (1.2–13 m). Before spawning, the male cleans an area of rock around a clump of red seaweed on which the female lays her eggs. The young garibaldi is orange red with blue blotches that begin to disappear when the fish reaches a length of about 2½ inches (6.5 cm). The blotches completely disappear by the time the fish has become an adult.

Not all damselfish are brightly colored. A few species are brown, black or gray. Some species are brightly colored when juveniles but become less colorful with age.

Clownfish, such as Premnas biaculeatus, live in close association with sea anemones. They shelter from predators among the anemones' stinging tentacles and are not harmed by their hosts.

Surviving the sting

The best-known damselfish are the 27 species of the genus *Amphiprion* and the single species of the genus *Premnas* known as clownfish or anemonefish. Clownfish shelter among the tentacles of a giant anemone that can span 4 feet (1.2 m). Other damselfish also have this habit but clownfish are the best-known for their association with sea anemones. They may leave the anemone to swim elsewhere but at the first sign of danger the fish dash back to take refuge among the tentacles. Experts believe that when the clownfish return to the shelter of the anemone's tentacles, any predatory fish that are in pursuit are caught, held by the tentacles and devoured by the anemone. The clownfish subsequently pick up fragments from the anemone's meal. Clownfish remain with the same anemone for life and rarely stray farther than 3–6½ feet (0.9–2 m) from their host.

A protective layer of mucus prevents the clownfish from being stung by their host anemone. For some time there was considerable debate as to whether some damselfish were innately immune to the stinging tentacles of anemones while others had to adjust to the stings, a process known as acclimation. In recent studies, "naive" damselfish (those bred in complete isolation from anemones) were forced into contact with three species of anemones: *Macrodactyla doreensis*, *Heteractis crispa* and *Stichodactyla haddoni*. Clownfish of the species

Amphiprion clarkii proved immune to the stings of all three anemone species. The species *A. ocellaris* and *A. perideraion* received stings from some species of anemone, though not from others. The experiment indicates that some species of damselfish are innately protected from the stings of some anemones, those which would naturally be their hosts, but must develop immunity to the stings of others.

Some scientists believe that clownfish acquire mucus from their host anemone's own mucus layer and that this enables the fish to mimic the host and so avoid being stung. Other experts argue that clownfish produce their own mucus protective layer to prevent stinging. In studies, scientists discovered that the mucus layer of "associated" *A. clarkii* damselfish (those that had lived with sea anemones) did contain anemone antigens (toxins or enzymes capable of producing an immune response). The mucus of naive clownfish of the same species did not contain these antigens. This indicates that innately protected clownfish do not produce a mucus coat that is biochemically similar to that of its host. It seems that innately protected clownfish acquire anemone substances by association with anemones. However scientists are still unsure whether these substances provide damselfish with the initial protection from host clownfish stings that the fish gradually become accustomed to, or whether the antigens give extra protection to innately protected fish.

DAMSELFLY

ALTHOUGH THE TERM "dragonfly" is frequently used to describe the insect order Odonata, the two main suborders, Zygoptera and Anisoptera, are better designated by the use of separate English names, damselfly and dragonfly, respectively. Damselflies are smaller and usually more slender than dragonflies. Many damselfly species have brightly colored bodies, often metallic green, blue or red. The wings may be colorless and transparent or colorfully tinted. In some species only the males have colored and patterned wings, whereas those of the female are transparent. At rest damselflies hold their wings erect over the back.

Unlike dragonflies, damselflies are not strong fliers. Both groups have very short antennae, but compensate for this by having very good vision. As they have relatively feeble flight, damselflies are seldom found far from the water in which they breed. Ponds, ditches, marshes and canals with a thick growth of reeds and water plants are damselflies' favorite habitat.

Fastidious insects

Most insects frequently clean the eyes and antennae with the forelegs, much as a cat washes its face using its paws. Damselflies are particularly thorough cleaners. They not only clean the sense organs of the head but use the hind legs to clean the end of the abdomen. Often the abdomen itself is curved and raised so as to stroke the wings and divide them from each other. The probable reason for this is that the long, weakly muscled wings may get stuck together by drifting threads of spider gossamer.

Like dragonflies, damselflies are extremely active insects and require a steady food supply to preserve their energy levels. Adult damselflies feed on small insects, both in the air and at rest, and the larvae probably feed on small aquatic insects and worms. Although neither swift nor strong, adults usually hunt small flying insects on the wing, as dragonflies often do, and scoop their prey into their jaws using their long legs. They probably feed mainly on gnats and midges.

Aerial courtship dances

Some kinds of damselflies perform courtship displays before mating. In the banded agrion, *Agrion splendens*, the male waits for a female to fly past and then signals to her by raising his body and spreading his wings. If this succeeds and she comes to rest near him, he performs an aerial fluttering dance backward and forward, facing her all the time, and then comes to rest and mates with her. The banded agrion is one of the species in which the wings are conspicuously colored in the male but not in the female, and it seems likely that this difference in the sexes is associated with courtship display. Coloration plays an important part in damselfly courtship. Bright colors signal a healthy mate whereas faded colors indicate that the insect may have passed its sexual prime.

The method of mating used by damselflies and dragonflies is unique among insects. The opening of the male's internal sexual organs is in the usual insect position, near the tip of the abdomen. Before mating he transfers sperm to a complicated accessory sexual organ on the underside of the front part of the abdomen, just behind the thorax. When pairing he first grasps the female's neck with a pair of claspers at the tip of his abdomen. Both insects then bend their bodies so as to bring the end of the female's abdomen into contact with the male accessory organ, and the sperm is transferred.

The female lays the fertilized eggs in the tissues of water plants through a sawlike ovipositor. This often takes place immediately after mating and sometimes before the male has released his hold on the female. In some species

When at rest, damselflies fold their wings along their body or hold them erect as butterflies do.

DAMSELFLIES

CLASS	**Insecta**
ORDER	**Odonata**
SUBORDER	**Zygoptera**
FAMILY	**Lestidae; Calopterygidae; various others**
GENUS AND SPECIES	**Many**

ALTERNATIVE NAMES
Demoiselle (Calopterygidae only); dancer; damsel; bluet; firetail; sprite; blue arrow

LENGTH
Body: up to 5 in. (12.5 cm), usually about 1½ in. (4 cm); wingspan: up to 7½ in. (19 cm), usually about 2 in. (5 cm)

DISTINCTIVE FEATURES
Very slender body; 2 pairs of wings of equal size, with intricate network of veins; at rest wings held flat over body; large, widely separated eyes; many species red, metallic blue or metallic green

DIET
Adult: small insects, especially gnats and midges. Larva: small aquatic invertebrates.

BREEDING
Varies according to species. Larval period: usually 1–2 years (temperate regions), 40–60 days (Tropics).

LIFE SPAN
Adult: usually less than 30 days

HABITAT
Many aquatic habitats, including ponds, lakes, marshes, rivers, ditches and streams

DISTRIBUTION
Virtually worldwide, especially in Tropics

STATUS
Most species common; 30 species threatened

Damselflies can mate both in the air and on a surface. The characteristic shape formed by the coupling of the male and female during mating is known as the wheel.

the two, coupled in this way, crawl down the stem of a reed into the water and descend together to a depth of 1 foot (30 cm) or more before the eggs are laid.

Underwater larvae

The minute creature that hatches from a damselfly egg can neither swim nor crawl and is known as the prolarva or pronymph. Within a few minutes, sometimes almost immediately after hatching, it sheds its skin and the first active larval stage is produced. The larva spends its life in the water and grows by shedding its skin at intervals, as do most insects. The larva may molt between 9 and 15 times during the course of its growth and may reach a length of 2–2½ inches (5–6 cm). It has a long body, not unlike that of an adult damselfly in shape, though the larva has no wings. At its rear end are three leaflike external gills. These contain a network of minute tubes, or tracheae, into which oxygen diffuses from the water. Respiration also takes place through the skin, rectum and wing sheaths.

In temperate regions, the life cycle of most of the smaller damselflies takes a year to complete, while that of some of the larger species may take up to two years. In the Tropics, the development of damselflies is more rapid and there may be several generations in a year. When growth is complete, the larvae crawl out of the water up onto a stone or a plant stem. They wait for a short time, until the skin of the back splits. The wings are expanded and hardened and the insects are able to fly within an hour or two. The period of time that the larvae spend underwater

varies between species and according to environmental conditions. Species that live in warm waters with plentiful food develop more quickly than those living in waters that are cooler or that lack nutrients. As a result, the larval stage may last for only 40 days or for as long as 6 years.

Several species of the genus *Megalagrion*, which are native to Hawaii, spend all or part of their time on land. The larvae of one species, *M. oahuense*, have hairy appendages instead of the leaflike tail gills common to other damselflies and are unable to swim.

DAPHNIA

THE WATER FLEA, DAPHNIA, is a crustacean, and is a distant relative of crabs and shrimps. It has a hard external skeleton and jointed appendages and limbs. The head has a large central eye, which is in fact two eyes joined together. It also has two pairs of antennae, one small and the other large, which are branched and used in swimming. Numbers of daphnia are often seen as a cloud of dancing specks in ponds and aquariums, or even as a surface scum. The largest species grows to only ⅕ inch (5 mm) long.

Each daphnia has five pairs of limbs, in constant motion, each flattened and bearing a complex arrangement of feathered bristles. These limbs lie in a space under the body bounded by the carapace, which looks like the shell of a bivalve mollusk. This also forms a brood pouch in the female. The carapace is transparent and is drawn out into a spine at its hind end.

Reacts to red light

Daphnia feeds on bacteria and single-celled algae in the water. It has to filter large amounts of water to strain these particles, which it does by rhythmically beating its legs, thereby pumping water through the space under its carapace. The bristles on the legs serve as strainers.

Its sensitivity to different colored light enables daphnia to place itself where the concentrations of algae are greatest. When sunlight shines through a patch of green algae in the water, much of the blue light is removed so that the light passing through is more red. When daphnia is exposed to red light in the laboratory, it will spend much of its time "dancing" upright in the water and moving horizontally very little. In blue light it tends to swim horizontally. If daphnia arrives by chance among algae, the slight redness of the light causes it to "dance" in that spot, where its food is plentiful. Where the light is less red, daphnia swims horizontally, thereby improving its chance of finding food.

Daphnia spends much of its time bobbing up and down in the water, head uppermost, sinking down a short way and then driving itself up again with a downward stroke of its large branched antennae. Like many other creatures living in the upper waters of seas and lakes, daphnia also migrates up and down every day to different depths. At dusk, the movement is upward, but during the night the whole population may gradually sink, only to rise again at dawn. Then, as the sun shines more brightly, it once more retreats to deeper water.

Males not essential

The female daphnia carries her eggs in a brood pouch. At certain times she lays eggs that can survive drying and freezing to hatch out months or years later. These are known as resting eggs. The resting eggs carry the populations over the winter and hatch in spring to give a generation of females only. These grow after each molt. Molts occur daily at first and there are about 17 during a lifetime. After each molt the animal swells by taking in water before growing a new cuticle (skin). After five to seven molts, a female begins to lay up to 30 eggs, which develop without being fertilized. They are kept in the brood pouch, the growing embryos being nourished by the yolk in the egg and also by secretions from the mother's body. As the season advances, the water warms up, the quantity of algae increases, growth of the daphnia speeds up and the population of females increases.

With the population rise, food becomes short and males are hatched, less than half the size of the females and slightly different in shape. Any eggs now laid are fertilized and these are of the resting type. They are fewer per female, larger and thick-shelled. Part of the carapace containing them forms a protective case that is shed at the next molt along with the eggs.

As summer ends the quantity of algae again increases, the daphnia population builds up, there is overcrowding and more males appear.

Under a microscope the winter or "resting" eggs carried by female daphnia are clearly visible through the transparent carapace.

Resting eggs are once more produced, and these survive the winter to restart the population the following spring. A few females may last the winter too. Living less actively at a low temperature, these grow largest and live longest. Only unsuitable conditions cause the appearance of males and resting eggs and hundreds of generations can be reared without any males appearing.

Variations in appearance

In some species of daphnia striking changes sometimes occur in the appearance of individual animals. These changes can be so great that, until their true nature was recognized in about 1890, individuals of a single species, indeed of a single population, were assigned to different genera because of the wide variation in their appearance. Some of the changes are due to age and reproductive condition and to changes in the environment, but most dramatic are the annual changes in form, a condition known as cyclomorphosis. The effect may be that a winter form will have a small head with the eye at the front, while in the summer form that part of the head in front of the eye grows forward as a long helmet.

Another factor that may cause individuals to vary in appearance is the amount of oxygen in the water. When humans live for a while at high altitude, where the air they breathe contains less oxygen, their bodies are stimulated to produce more hemoglobin in order to carry oxygen in the blood from lungs to tissues. Changes in daphnia living in poorly aerated water are reflected in a color change in the animal's body. There may be as much as a twelvefold increase in the hemoglobin levels of daphnia in poorly oxygenated waters, as opposed to an increase of only about one-fifth in humans living at high altitude. The warmer the water, or the less oxygen there is in it, the redder the daphnia become.

A daphnia's four branched antennae enable the animal to swim through the water. Its 10 food-gathering limbs are protected by the large carapace.

DAPHNIA

PHYLUM	**Arthropoda**
CLASS	**Crustacea**
ORDER	**Cladocera**
FAMILY	**Daphniidae**
GENUS AND SPECIES	***Daphnia magna*; others**

ALTERNATIVE NAME
Water flea

LENGTH
Up to ⅕ in. (5 mm); female larger than male

DISTINCTIVE FEATURES
Tiny: barely visible to naked human eye; 2 pairs of long, branched antennae; 5 pairs of flattened limbs; 2 eyes fused, giving appearance of single central eye; transparent carapace (shell)

DIET
Bacteria, algae and other small zooplankton

BREEDING
Parthenogenetic reproduction. Number of eggs: 2 to 8 per molt.

LIFE SPAN
Up to 100 days

HABITAT
Fresh water, mainly in upper part of water column

DISTRIBUTION
Worldwide

STATUS
Superabundant

DARTER

DARTERS ARE VERY MUCH LIKE cormorants in shape, although they have longer, more slender necks, usually carried in a Z-shaped posture, and long, stiletto-like bills, each mandible of which has a cutting edge. They favor the warm, quiet waters of the tropical and subtropical regions of North and South America, Africa, Madagascar, Asia and Australasia. The American species is called the anhinga, a word derived from the language of Amazonian native peoples. Darters are closely related to cormorants and some ornithologists consider the two groups to be part of the same family.

Darters are distinguishable from other species of waterbird by their long tails and corrugated outer tail feathers. The short legs have long toes that are linked by webbing. The plumage is generally dark with a metallic sheen, and the female usually has paler underparts. There are four species of darter that differ slightly in color but are otherwise very similar. The American anhinga, *Anhinga anhinga*, ranges from the southern borders of the United States south to northern Argentina. The African darter, *A. rufa*, is found in Africa south of the Sahara, the Middle East and Madagascar. The oriental, or Indian, darter, *A. melanogaster*, lives in India and

Southeast Asia and the Australian darter, *A. novaehollandiae*, is found in Australia and New Guinea. Darters are strong fliers and are migratory in some areas. Movements are usually related to regional food shortages caused by changes in the weather.

Freshwater divers

Unlike their relatives the cormorants, which live mainly in coastal waters, darters inhabit freshwater lakes, rivers and swamps. They stay around the wooded edges and banks, where they may be seen perching in the trees with their wings spread in the manner of cormorants. Only rarely are they seen in the brackish waters of estuaries and lagoons. Darters are strong swimmers, capable of propelling themselves swiftly forward with their webbed feet. They often swim at the water's surface with only head and sinuous neck visible. This habit has given rise to their alternative name: snakebirds.

Like loons and grebes, darters can change their buoyancy. This is achieved by two methods. The plumage can be flattened against the body, thereby squeezing out air trapped between the feathers. This air is essential to all waterbirds to keep them fully afloat. If a duck,

The darters' habit of extending their large wings in order to rearrange the feathers is a characteristic shared with the closely related cormorants.

In common with other darters, the American anhinga favors quiet, wooded shorelines for nesting.

AMERICAN ANHINGA

CLASS	**Aves**
ORDER	**Pelecaniformes**
FAMILY	**Anhingidae**
GENUS AND SPECIES	***Anhinga anhinga***

ALTERNATIVE NAME
Snakebird

WEIGHT
About 3 lb. (1.4 kg)

LENGTH
Head to tail: 31½–35 in. (80–90 cm); wingspan: 4 ft. (1.2 m)

DISTINCTIVE FEATURES
Long, slender neck; long, sharply pointed bill; long tail; webbed feet. Male: mainly black plumage with greenish gloss; bold white wingbar. Female: pale gray-buff head, neck and upper chest.

DIET
Mainly fish; also amphibians, reptiles and invertebrates, especially crustaceans

BREEDING
Age at first breeding: 2 years; breeding season: all year (Tropics), spring and summer (North America); number of eggs: 3 to 5; incubation period: 25–28 days; fledging period: about 42 days; breeding interval: 1 year

LIFE SPAN
Up to 9 years

HABITAT
Lakes, swamps and slow-moving rivers; occasionally estuaries and tidal inlets

DISTRIBUTION
Coastal areas, from Florida west to Texas; Mexico south to northern Argentina

STATUS
Common

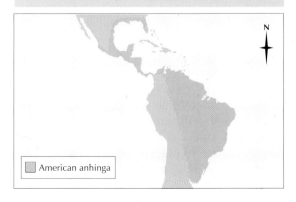

American anhinga

for instance, has the waterproofing layer of oil removed from its feathers by detergent, it loses most of its buoyancy. Diving birds also reduce their buoyancy by exhaling air from the air sacs. These are a series of thin-walled, balloonlike extensions of the lungs that spread through the body. The air sacs are known to play an important part in the birds' breathing systems, but the way in which they function remains uncertain.

Spearfishers

Darters hunt underwater for fish, frogs, newts, crustaceans and aquatic insects. The anhinga even catches very young alligators. Large prey is caught by impaling it on the bill with a swift

Waterside nests

forward strike of the head; the bill is kept slightly open during this action. After catching its prey, the darter surfaces and throws it off the bill with a quick flick of the head, catching it deftly and then juggling it into position in order to swallow it, head foremost. This fundamentally instinctive action requires practice to be perfected. Young darters frequently experience difficulty in removing fish that are firmly speared or else lose the fish when they are shaken off.

When a darter stalks up to its prey, it moves its neck forward and backward, then rapidly straightens the neck to thrust its head forward in a swift strike. The speed of the strike is achieved by a trigger mechanism in the characteristic Z-shape of the neck, which is built like an extendable arm with a hinge on either side of the eighth cervical vertebrae. These joints cannot be straightened out completely without tearing muscles or tendons, but they can bend a considerable amount. To strike, the darter draws its head back by tendons running the length of the neck and passing through a pulley mechanism on one of the vertebrae just behind the joints. Then, having aimed, the head is shot forward by a powerful muscle straightening the joints.

This spearfishing technique does not allow darters to catch the largest and most agile fish, and even those caught often need to be subdued by being beaten against a branch before they can be swallowed. Darters also use their bill in the manner of a pair of forceps, to pick insects off the surface of the water.

Darters nest in small colonies in trees and bushes, usually overhanging water. They often nest alongside other waterbirds, such as herons and ibises. The same nests are frequently used year after year, though it is not unusual for a colony to shift from one part of a lake or river to another in succeeding years. When old nests are being used, the males claim them at the start of the breeding season and defend them against rivals, though other bird species are tolerated.

To attract a female to his nest, a male darter slowly waves his wings, stretching and closing each one alternately to show off their conspicuous coloring. He may also grab a twig in his bill and vigorously wave it to attract her attention. Having attracted a female and courted her, he collects twigs from nearby trees and bushes that she weaves into the nest.

Breeding occurs year-round in favorable climates and the first egg is laid 2–3 days after the start of a new nest. Both parents incubate the three to five eggs for about 1 month. The chicks hatch out naked and blind but grow coats of white or pale buff down within a couple of days. In 2 weeks they are capable of leaving the nest if disturbed, to plunge into the water and swim away. When the danger is over, they attempt to climb back to the nest or, if their efforts are unsuccessful, scramble out onto a rock or log, using their neck and wings for leverage as well as their feet. The parents feed them in their new refuge until they are fledged, at 6–8 weeks.

Darters (oriental darter, above) often swim with the body submerged and only the slender neck and head above water. This has given rise to their alternative name of snakebirds.

DARWIN'S FINCHES

Darwin's finches evolved on the isolated Galapagos Islands in the eastern Pacific. Each species has a differently shaped bill, suited to its particular diet. Some species eat insects, others seeds and fruits, while two feed on flower nectar.

IN 1835 THE ENGLISH NATURALIST Charles Darwin visited the Galapagos Islands during his tour of South America on H.M.S. *Beagle*. His study of the finches that he found there, which were subsequently named after him, provided one of the main sources of inspiration for his theory of evolution by natural selection. The ancestors of the finches had presumably been blown to the islands by high winds. Once established they were able to evolve into several distinct forms, to take advantage of the range of different habitats and resources, or ecological niches, available on the islands. The divergence from the ancestral finches to the 14 modern species is evident in many aspects of their lives. It is difficult to discuss their bodily form without reference to Darwin's theory of evolution.

Darwin's finches are a family of birds that lives almost exclusively on the Galapagos Islands; one of the species lives on Cocos Island some 600 miles (970 km) to the northeast. They are presumed to have originated from now-extinct finches native to mainland South America, which lies 600 miles eastward.

The finches' plumage is grayish brown with occasional patches of black on the males of certain species. Of the 14 species there is little variation except in the bills. This is unusual, as on the mainland finches usually differ in plumage as well as body form.

Food must fit the bill

The bills of Darwin's finches range in shape from slender to stout and are adapted for eating different kinds of food. There are few species of birds native to the Galapagos Islands, so the immigrant ancestors of the finches found little competition and were able to invade specific ecological niches. In so doing they developed habits similar to those birds that fill the same kinds of niche on the mainland. For example, on the Galapagos Islands, there is the warbler-finch, *Certhidea olivacea*, and the woodpecker-finch, *Camarhynchus pallidus*, and other finches that are titlike or parrotlike.

None of the finch species has taken to water, although one forages for small crustaceans on the seashore. Neither have any of the species become

DARWIN'S FINCHES

CLASS	**Aves**
ORDER	**Passeriformes**
FAMILY	**Fringillidae**
GENUS	**Ground finches, *Geospiza*; tree finches (including woodpecker-finch), *Camarhynchus*; warbler-finches, *Certhidea*; mangrove finches, *Cactospiza*; vegetarian finches, *Platyspiza*; Cocos Island finch, *Pinaroloxias***
SPECIES	**14 species**

ALTERNATIVE NAME
Galapagos finches

LENGTH
Head to tail: 4–6 in. (10–15 cm)

DISTINCTIVE FEATURES
Sparrow-sized; short, rounded wings; short tail; dull plumage in shades of brown, gray and black; bill varies according to species

DIET
Varies between species; diets include: ticks, spiders, insects, small crustaceans, fruits, seeds, flower nectar (*G. scandens* and *G. conirostris* only) and blood (*G. difficilis* only)

BREEDING
Age at first breeding: 1 year; breeding season: usually December–April, depending on rainfall; number of eggs: 2 to 5; incubation period: about 12 days; fledging period: 13–14 days; breeding interval: depends on environmental conditions

LIFE SPAN
Probably up to about 5 years

HABITAT
Most species in particular vegetation zone

DISTRIBUTION
Islands of the Galapagos Archipelago; Cocos Island (*Pinaroloxias* only)

STATUS
All populations small, but not threatened

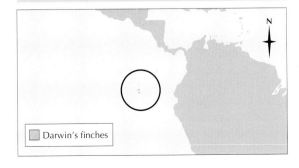

Darwin's finches

regular flesh-eaters. However, one species with a sharp bill, *Geospiza difficilis*, has been seen to go to a nesting booby (a large seabird related to gannets), puncture its skin and drink its blood. This species has also been seen to eat gulls' eggs and the half-digested fish mixture that boobies feed to their young.

The ground finches (*Geospiza* spp.) have stout bills, and use them for cracking seeds, but they also eat fruits, flowers and caterpillars. Within this group there is a gradation of bill sizes, the size of the bill determining the food taken. These species are most like the typical finches found elsewhere, which are a family of seed-eaters.

The warbler-finch hunts for small insects, sometimes catching them in the air in the manner of true warblers. Warbler-finches even have the habit of continually flicking their wings, a common characteristic of warblers.

Probes with a cactus spine

The tree finches (*Camarhynchus*) have pointed bills and behave in a similar manner to tits. They hop nimbly among twigs, sometimes hanging upside down, investigating bark and leaves for beetles and other small insects.

One species of tree finch, the woodpecker-finch, specializes in searching trees and bushes for insect larvae. Having found their quarry, true woodpeckers insert a long tongue into the hole to prize out the insect. Woodpecker-finches do not have a long tongue. Instead, they snap off a twig or cactus spine and, holding it in the bill, use it to extract the insect. This behavior provides an

The warbler-finch has evolved a thin, pointed bill, the perfect shape for catching small spiders and insects.

The woodpecker-finch uses twigs and (above) cactus spines to extract insect larvae from tree bark. Such examples of tool using are rare among birds.

extremely rare example of tool use among birds. Woodpecker-finches also establish stores of cactus spines for future use.

Similar nesting habits

By contrast to the wide variation in feeding habits, the nesting habits of Darwin's finches are similar. Their nests are built the same height above ground, usually at 3–30 feet (1–10 m), and are similar in construction. They are bulky and are made of materials such as twigs, grasses and lichens, with domed roofs to protect the broods from the heat of the tropical sun.

During the breeding season, which coincides with the rains, the finches defend territories against birds of their own species. Mates are attracted by a song and by displays that usually take place around the nest. The usual clutch consists of four white eggs with pink spots. These are incubated for about 12 days by the female, which is fed by the male.

Few native predators

Small birds generally have a host of predators, including larger birds, mammals and reptiles. However, the only predators of Darwin's finches, apart from domestic cats introduced by humans, are the Galapagos owl (a subspecies of the short-eared owl, *Asio flammeus*) and the Galapagos hawk, *Buteo galapagoensis*. On some islands the owl rarely takes any finches, but on others it kills them regularly. The hawk catches only the occasional fledgling finch.

Darwin's finches are very tame toward humans and usually fail to recognize domestic cats as being a danger. It is thought that on the Galapagos Island of Indefatigable, domestic cats were probably responsible for the extinction of one species of ground-living finch there.

Darwin's inspiration

The process whereby the ancestral finches evolved into the different types of finches that live on the Galapagos Islands today is known as adaptive radiation. Scientists use the term adaptive to describe the way in which the changes an individual species undergoes over time suit it to a particular way of life. These changes are molded by certain forces that Darwin realized were vital in the evolution of species.

Once the ancestors of Darwin's finches had arrived on the Galapagos Islands, they no longer mixed with other finch species from the mainland. Isolation helps speciation (the development of species with their individual characteristics), although it is not a prerequisite. There may be more than one species of finch on any one of the Galapagos Islands, indicating that ancestral birds living side by side evolved different adaptations for the different resources available on that island. Darwin's finches have had plentiful resources available to them because there are few competitors and predators present in an island environment compared to on the mainland. The finches have not had to compete with woodpeckers, tits, warblers and other birds for food, shelter and nesting sites. Consequently a phenomenon called sympatric speciation has occurred: resources are sufficient for species to be able to thrive independently of one another without any loss of identity from interbreeding.

There may have been a number of behavioral isolation mechanisms that co-evolved alongside the finches' feeding habits. These types of behavior may have acted as barriers to breeding between the ancestral populations that occupied different ecological niches. In the ancestral populations there would have been a selective advantage for any species that had a behavioral mechanism to produce offspring possessing exclusive access to unexploited resources. For example, variants that had bills well-adapted to a food resource that was not vigorously competed for would do well, in Darwinian terms, to breed among themselves.

In the Galapagos Islands predators have not had a significant impact on the evolution of Darwin's finches. As a result, it is the birds' feeding methods that have altered over time, in order that the different species could make the best use of the available food resources. The islands' unique environment has meant that Darwin's finches have been able to specialize in both food sources and habitats. Over time competition between species has been reduced.

DEAD MAN'S FINGERS

DEAD MAN'S FINGERS, sometimes called sea fingers, is better known to zoologists under its scientific name, *Alcyonium*. It is a type of soft coral, closely related to the hard or stony corals that form tropical reefs. Dead man's fingers grows in colonies (groups) of polyps (cylindrical structures of tissue). Each colony grows from a single polyp that buds and makes copies of itself. The colony is a tough, jellylike mass colored white to orange and made up of a central mass from which spring thick, fingerlike lobes. The number of lobes varies but often a colony has four to five fingers and is the size of a human fist. The appearance of such a colony has given rise to the species' common name.

A colony contains many polyps, each one of which resembles a miniature sea anemone except that the eight tentacles have side branches and so are featherlike. Eight mesenteries (membranous partitions) divide the central cavity of the polyp. Instead of the hard, stony skeleton of a true coral, *Alcyonium* has a skeleton of a rubberlike mass supported by separate internal spicules (literally, little spikes) made of calcium carbonate (chalk). These spicules are needle-shaped and ornamented with knobs and spikes.

Size depends on depth

The name dead man's fingers, or dead man's toes, has been used by fishers for more than 200 years. In his *Natural History of the Corallines* (1755), the English naturalist John Ellis reported that this coral was often brought up in nets by fishers seeking flatfish. The colonies usually grow on stable, hard surfaces and the size that they attain depends on the depth at which they are growing. In waters of 45–60 feet (14–18 m) they are usually 1.5–2 inches (4–5 cm) long when contracted. At depths of 60–90 feet (18–27 m), they grow to 3–4 inches (7.5–10 cm) long. Underwater they expand, taking in water and swelling. The polyps also expand so instead of looking like "dead man's fingers," they resemble miniature flower clumps when covered with delicate eight-rayed polyps.

The reason for the differences in size is that in shallower waters there is more wave and current action. At a certain size the colonies tend to be overturned, become buried in silt and die. In many areas *Alcyonium* on stones and shells have been much reduced by dredging and trawling. In sheltered places among rocks and on pier piles, they can grow unmolested. Large specimens are sometimes seen uncovered at extreme low spring tides.

On large rocks swept by strong currents, *Alcyonium* has excellent feeding conditions and consequently dense aggregations of large colonies are able to flourish, which may grow up to 12 inches (30 cm). Dead man's fingers need a solid support to grow from and cannot survive if this support is taken away. Those colonies that settle on pebbles do not last long; the pebbles roll over as a result of the growth of the colony.

Often orange or pale pink in color, dead man's fingers are related to sea anemones, which also belong to the class Anthozoa. The two groups frequently live side by side.

DEAD MAN'S FINGERS

PHYLUM	**Cnidaria**
CLASS	**Anthozoa**
ORDER	**Alcyonacea**
FAMILY	**Alcyoniidae**
GENUS AND SPECIES	***Alcyonium digitatum***

ALTERNATIVE NAMES
Sea fingers; dead man's toes

LENGTH
Usually up to 8 in. (20 cm)

DISTINCTIVE FEATURES
Irregularly branched, thick, fleshy lobes; 3 color forms: yellow, orange and pinkish white; lives in colonies (groups)

DIET
Mainly zooplankton; also phytoplankton

BREEDING
Sexes normally separate, some colonies hermaphroditic; larval period: many weeks

LIFE SPAN
At least 25 years

HABITAT
On rocks and shells in shallow seas up to 165 ft. (50 m) deep, especially where strong currents occur

DISTRIBUTION
Coastal waters from Iceland and Norway south to Portugal

STATUS
Common

Dead man's fingers is a species of soft coral. Unlike true corals, it has a soft, jellylike skeleton from which the polyps sprout.

A communal stomach

The tentacles of each polyp trap small swimming animals, paralyze them with their stinging cells and pass them on to the mouth, as in anemones. Smaller organisms, such as phytoplankton, are also filtered using a combination of mucus and cilia (fine hairs). The body of the colony is honeycombed with a system of tubes that connects each polyp with the rest. Food caught by one is therefore shared with the rest, so a colony can flourish as long as enough polyps catch food. It is not necessary for all to be feeding all the time.

Growth by budding

Adult colonies are generally male or female, although a few are hermaphrodites. Eggs and sperm are shed into the water and some of the eggs eventually become fertilized, producing swimming larvae. Each larva is oval, the body being covered with cilia, which drive it along by beating in unison. When a larva settles on a particular site, it changes into a polyp. A bud appears on its side and grows into a mature polyp, still attached to the parent. Repeated budding forms a colony.

Very few animals feed off dead man's fingers. Its polyps are sometimes eaten by two species of sea slugs, both belonging to the genus *Tritonia*. *T. hombergi*, which grows up to 8 inches (20 cm) long, may be able to inflict some damage on a colony, but scientists do not believe that such actions permanently harm the coral.

Hibernation

Coral colonies often briefly retract their polyps if they are disturbed or conditions are unfavorable. However, every year dead man's fingers spends

Dead man's fingers

weeks or even months with its polyps retracted in a resting state similar to hibernation. During this period, the colony's surface becomes discolored and leatherlike in appearance. A thin film of algae grows over the colony and it appears to be lifeless. However, after some time, the skin flakes off as the polyps re-emerge to feed once more.

DEEP–SEA ANGLERFISH

THE DEEP-SEA ANGLERFISH differ from other anglerfish in a variety of ways. Two notable distinctions are that they have no pelvic fins and live in midwater in deep, oceanic waters instead of exclusively on the seabed in shallow waters. Deep-sea anglerfish are most abundant at depths of about 6,000 feet (1,830 m). There is a considerable difference in size between the sexes. In some species the female is many thousand times the size of the male. The first ray of the dorsal fin has moved forward onto the head, as in shallow-water anglerfish, and has been modified into a form of fishing rod. However, in deep-sea anglerfish only the females have this rod and it has a luminous tip to serve as a lure for prey.

Due to the marked differences between shallow-water and deep-sea anglerfish, they are placed in separate superfamilies. The superfamily containing the deep-sea species, Ceratioidea, is subdivided into 11 families. The members of these families are similar in form and habits but differ in such details as length of rod, shape of lure and size of fins.

Sea devils

Scientists first became aware of the existence of deep-sea anglerfish from a specimen washed ashore on the west coast of Greenland some time before 1844. The fish, one of a group of deep-sea anglerfish now known as sea devils, was found by Lieutenant-Commander C. Holbøll of the Royal Danish Navy. It was named *Ceratias holboelli* after him. This species has become one of the best-known anglerfish and is widely distributed throughout the world's oceans. The female *C. holboelli* is 3½ feet (1 m) long, black in color and has a rough skin. Her body is pear-shaped, with a large head and gaping mouth. With the exception of the tail fin, all of her fins are small, the dorsal and anal fins having strong spines with a thin tissue between the spines. As the shape of her body and fins suggests, the female is not a strong swimmer and remains passively floating in the water for much of the time.

The lure of the light

The female deep-sea anglerfish lures its prey into its huge mouth with the glowing lure that grows from its head. Some female deep-sea anglerfish have movable lures. *C. holboelli* is able to withdraw its lure into a groove running along its

head and back. Although it has not been possible for scientists to study the behavior of a live fish, it seems likely that *C. holboelli* can "play" its prey, possibly waving its light slightly to attract a smaller fish, then withdrawing the rod slowly into the groove, enticing the prey nearer and nearer to the powerful jaws. Scientists believe that deep-sea anglerfish prey on smaller fish, prawns and euphausians, deep-sea relatives of the prawnlike krill on which some whales feed.

The light in the lure of the female deep-sea anglerfish is probably under her control. The Danish zoologist E. Bertelsen has suggested that the luminous bacteria in the cavity of the lure flash when supplied with extra oxygen. Blood vessels run into this cavity and if the flow of blood is increased, the bacteria light up; their light fades when blood is withdrawn again.

Parasitic mates

Four deep-sea anglerfish families related to the genus *Ceratias* have an unusual method of reproduction. The males are free-swimming at first, with large eyes, no rod or lure and no digestive tube. They have a smooth skin and are diminutive in size: the largest specimen found to date was only ⅔ inches (2 cm) long. Male deep-sea anglerfish have large olfactory (smell) organs and scientists believe that they seek out mates of their own species by scenting characteristic secretion trails (pheromones) that the females emit.

Female deep-sea anglerfish attract their prey by means of the luminous rod that projects from the head. They are weak swimmers, and float in the water in wait for passing prey.

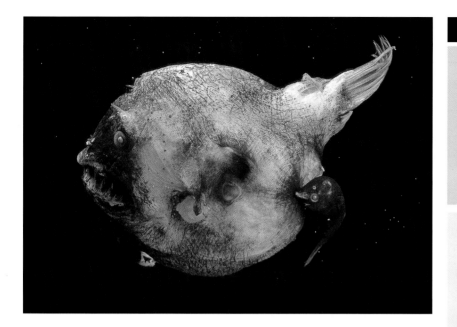

In several deep-sea anglerfish families the male reproduces by permanently attaching himself to the female. Their tissues fuse and the male degenerates, finally becoming nothing more than a sexual organ.

DEEP–SEA ANGLERFISH

CLASS	**Osteichthyes**
ORDER	**Lophiiformes**
SUPERFAMILY	**Ceratioidea**
FAMILY	**11, including sea devils, Ceratiidae**
GENUS	**35**
SPECIES	**149, including *Ceratias holboelli***

LENGTH
⅓–47 in. (1–120 cm); female many times larger than male

DISTINCTIVE FEATURES
All but 1 species black with luminescent areas on body; no pelvic fins. Female: luminescent lure on front of head; huge, powerful jaws with many large teeth.

DIET
Fish, squid, prawns and euphausians (deep-sea relatives of krill)

BREEDING
Poorly known. In 4 families, males parasitize females.

LIFE SPAN
Not known

HABITAT
Deep waters, in middle and lower levels

DISTRIBUTION
Subarctic to subantarctic seas and oceans, except Mediterranean and Black Sea

STATUS
Abundant

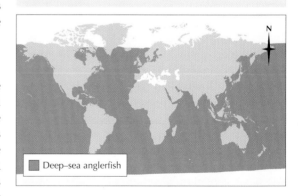

Deep–sea anglerfish

When a male meets a mature female he grips her skin with his hooked denticles (small, pointed teeth). Thereafter, the male's body begins to degenerate. His eyes become smaller and are eventually lost. His skin becomes spiny and around his jaws it fuses with the female's skin, leaving a small hole on each side of the mouth through which water is drawn for breathing. The female's blood vessels join with those of the male and he is nourished by the circulation of her blood through his body. This represents a form of placental feeding, similar to the way that a mammalian fetus is fed by the mother's blood circulating through the placenta. Meanwhile the male grows in size, possibly to a length of 6 inches (15 cm). Internally he grows large testes, the male reproductive organs.

In his book *Abyss*, the American scientist C. P. Idyll has pointed out that the largest known female of *C. holboelli* was half a million times as heavy as the smallest recorded male of the same species of deep-sea anglerfish.

Growth patterns

In the North Atlantic spawning occurs in the summer, possibly in deep water. The fertilized eggs are laid in strands that wrap around the female's body. However, it seems that the eggs must float upward during development because the fry, just over 3 millimeters long, are found in surface waters. These feed mainly on copepods (a type of crustacean). At this early stage in their life the young females differ from the young males in having a well-developed intestinal tract and the beginnings of a rod between the eyes.

By the time the male is just over 4 millimeters long, he has grown the special teeth on the snout and lower jaw that he will later use to grip the female's skin. He is also already considerably slimmer than the female. While these changes are taking place, the fish slowly descend to greater depths. Deep-sea anglerfish lack a swim bladder and, when young, have a layer of jellylike tissue under the skin for buoyancy. This layer of jelly is gradually lost, and this may be what causes them to descend into deep water.

DEER

APPROXIMATELY 38 MILLION YEARS AGO a group of herbivorous mammals known as the ungulates (animals with hooves) split into two groups: the artiodactyls, or even-toed ungulates, and the perissodactyls, or odd-toed ungulates. The perissodactyls today contain the horses, zebras and rhinoceroses. The artiodactyls are represented by nine families including the buffalo, pigs, giraffes and deer. The two families that contain deer are the Cervidae (true deer) and the Moschidae (musk deer), though another family, the Tragulidae (mouse deer), is often associated with them. There are 44 species within the two main families, 41 of which belong to the Cervidae.

Deer have many features in common, but the Cervidae are the most similar and instantly recognizable species. They all have fairly long bodies, slim legs and short tails. The large, triangular ears are toward the top of the head and the large eyes are to the sides. All deer have facial glands, which are used in identification and for marking out territories. Some species also have scent glands on the feet. Many deer are colored gray to reddish brown, though a few species are white or black. Newborn deer, which are called calves, fawns or kids according to species, often have light colored spots on a brown coat. This pattern acts as camouflage in dense vegetation.

Body size in deer varies considerably. The tiny northern Andean pudu, *Pudu mephistophiles*, weighs up to 20 pounds (10 kg) and stands up to 16 inches (40 cm) at the shoulder, while the Alaskan moose, *Alces alces gigas*, may weigh as

Wapiti stags attempt to establish dominance in rutting season by calling and by using their antlers to fight other males.

much as 1,500 pounds (680 kg) and stands 86 inches (2.2 m) at the shoulder. There is an unconfirmed record of an Alaskan moose weighing an estimated 2,600 pounds (1,180 kg).

Antlers

Another variation between deer can be seen in the antlers, the feature with which they are most commonly associated. In most species only the stags (males) possess antlers, although female reindeer, or caribou, *Rangifer tarandus*, develop smaller versions of antlers. The most primitive species, such as the Chinese water deer (*Hydropotes inermis*) and musk deer (genus *Moschus*) lack antlers and instead have protruding, fang-like incisors that are used during displays and fighting.

Antlers vary in appearance from the short, dagger-like protrusions of the muntjacs (genus *Muntiacus*)

CLASSIFICATION	
CLASS Mammalia	
ORDER Artiodactyla	
FAMILY Cervidae: true deer; Moschidae: musk deer	
NUMBER OF SPECIES 44	

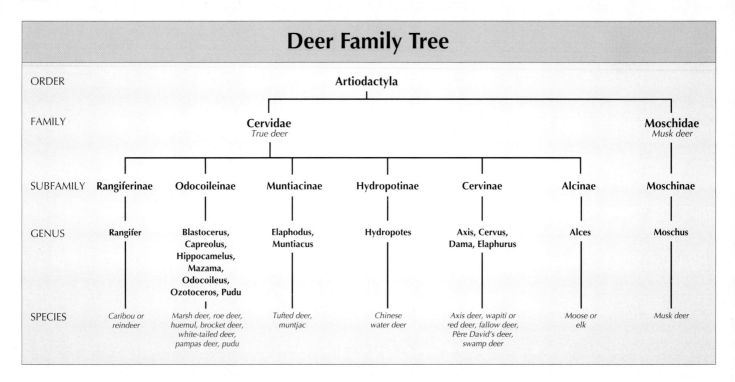

Deer Family Tree

ORDER	Artiodactyla						
FAMILY		Cervidae *True deer*					Moschidae *Musk deer*
SUBFAMILY	Rangiferinae	Odocoileinae	Muntiacinae	Hydropotinae	Cervinae	Alcinae	Moschinae
GENUS	Rangifer	Blastocerus, Capreolus, Hippocamelus, Mazama, Odocoileus, Ozotoceros, Pudu	Elaphodus, Muntiacus	Hydropotes	Axis, Cervus, Dama, Elaphurus	Alces	Moschus
SPECIES	*Caribou or reindeer*	*Marsh deer, roe deer, huemul, brocket deer, white-tailed deer, pampas deer, pudu*	*Tufted deer, muntjac*	*Chinese water deer*	*Axis deer, wapiti or red deer, fallow deer, Père David's deer, swamp deer*	*Moose or elk*	*Musk deer*

to the more elaborate palmate (hand-shaped) form of fallow deer (*Dama dama*) and moose and the spectacular, branched and multiple-pointed antlers of white-tailed deer (genus *Odocoileus*) and wapiti (*Cervus elaphus*). The largest and most elaborate antlers of all belonged to an extinct species formerly found across Europe and Siberia, the Irish elk, *Megaloceros*. Despite its common name, this species was neither solely of Irish origin nor an elk. It was a close relative of the fallow deer and had a set of enormous antlers with a 12-foot (3.7-m) span

that weighed nearly 1,000 pounds (45 kg). The antlers accounted for approximately one-seventh of the Irish elk's total body weight. Unlike most other deer, which generally favor woodland habitats, the Irish elk lived in a plains environment during the warm interglacial period that ended 12,000 years ago.

Deer cast and regrow their antlers annually. The antlers become larger and more elaborate with each year in most species. When a set of antlers first grows it is covered in a soft skin known as velvet that drops away when the set is fully grown. To shed and regrow antlers annually is an energetically demanding procedure. Wapiti eat their own discarded antlers to replace some of the minerals that are lost through this process. Other species eat their shed velvet for the same reason.

When the antlers are completely free of velvet the stags use them to display dominance during the rut (the mating season). This assertion of dominance may involve using the antlers to fight with another stag.

The rutting season

The evolutionary trend in deer toward more elaborate antler formation has been paralleled by the gradual progression toward a more polygynous society (a society

Female white-tailed deer give birth alone and live apart from the males while they tend the young. The fawns stay with their mothers until they are 2 years old.

in which a single adult male has a relationship with two or more adult females). Every stag attempts to mate with more than one female each breeding season, whereas the female generally mates once only. This results in competition among the males for the females.

During the rutting season wapiti stags pass through a series of stages of escalating aggression in order to avoid unnecessary damage caused by fighting. On observing another male in his territory, a stag bellows a long, deep roar. The other stag replies in the same manner and if one of the stags has an obviously higher-pitched roar, he is assessed as the smaller and less powerful male, loses the contest and resigns his right to mate with females in that area. If the roars are similar in pitch, the next stage, known as the parallel walk, takes place. The stags slowly walk up and down next to each other, presumably assessing one another's size. Again, if one stag is assessed as being smaller, he loses and withdraws. However, if the contest is still not resolved, sparring with the antlers may take place until one deer loses the fight or the antlers become locked in combat. The conflict progresses from a pushing match to barging and wrestling. Each stag can easily become gored or have limbs broken during this violent confrontation, though such physical injury is very much a last resort. Occasionally the clean skulls of stags that died with antlers still locked are found years after the rut took place.

The young are born 6–9 months after mating has taken place. Usually one to three young are produced. The young stay close to the mother for the first few months, though in nonherding species young females are encouraged by the mother to move away and set up their own ranges when about 1 year old. Alternatively the young are often violently

Swamp deer, **Cervus duvauceli,** *favor damp grasslands, such as floodplain meadows. Today much of their range is threatened by drainage schemes and land reclamation.*

pushed into less desirable environments by older, territorial males. Most species breed after 18 months but a few species, including some populations of roe deer, *Capreolus capreolus,* are able to breed after just 1 year.

Feeding strategies

All deer are herbivorous but most can be categorized as either grazers or browsers. The grazers include fallow deer and wapiti. They feed on grasses and plants on the ground but also take new twigs, leaves and bark from trees when more nutritious food is not available. Roe deer are browsers and feed on herbs, twigs, leaves and shoots. Most species have preferred food types that provide them with the maximum level of nutrition, and some have very specialized diets. Reindeer and caribou, for example, feed largely on reindeer moss, a branched, bushy lichen that grows abundantly in the Arctic regions of this species' range. Grazers frequently live in herds, whereas browsers are often solitary or live in very small groups. For example, fallow deer can live in herds of several hundred individuals, whereas roe deer tend to live alone or in small family groups of up to five individuals.

Distribution

Deer are more common in cooler climates but have a worldwide distribution. Native species exist in China (sika and musk deer), Siberia (musk deer), North America (white-tailed and mule deer, wapiti, moose and caribou), South

The southern Andean pudu, Pudu pudu, *is the smallest of all true deer, weighing no more than 17½ pounds (8 kg).*

America (brocket deer and pudu), Europe (fallow, red and roe deer), Iran (Persian fallow deer) and India, Indonesia and Malaysia (muntjac). Many species have been introduced into non-native countries and continents. This process has been spurred on by the considerable ornamental value of deer in parklands and by their perceived value as high quality game animals for hunting. One result of such an introduction is that wapiti now exist in Australia, New Zealand and parts of North Africa, regions that have no indigenous deer species.

Conservation

The need to preserve the many endangered forms of deer has recently acquired a higher profile, aided by greater public awareness of their vulnerability and of the essential role they play in maintaining natural environments within their ranges. Of the 44 species of deer, about half are listed as threatened by the I.U.C.N. (World Conservation Union), although in many cases a species at risk is represented by one or more subspecies. For example, the wapiti contains 12 subspecies, of which 6 are listed as endangered while the other 6 subspecies are either out of danger or abundant.

Despite conservation attempts, however, a number of full species are threatened with imminent extinction. The wild population of Fea's muntjac, *Muntiacus feae*, which is native to

Borneo and Thailand, is not known, but four were recorded in captivity in 1984. Numbers of the north Andean huemul, *Hippocamelus antisensis*, and the south Andean huemul, *H. bisculus*, have been much reduced by overhunting and habitat destruction. The latter is classified as endangered and some estimates place its population in the wild at 1,500. Although the status of Prince Alfred's deer, *Cervus unicolor alfredi*, in the Philippines is not known, conservationists believe that the wild population is very small. Schomburgk's deer, *C. schomburgki*, of Thailand, probably became extinct in the 1930s.

As with the vast majority of threatened mammals, deer populations are declining due to habitat loss. However, several species, such as the European roe deer and the white-tailed deer of North America, are increasing in number and range as more forests are replanted and as hunting becomes more regulated. Many deer species can become pests of agriculture, silviculture (the development and maintainance of forests) and even horticulture, often resulting in their persecution. It is thus increasingly important that deer populations are responsibly managed, especially as many of their natural predators have been exterminated within their natural ranges.

For particular species see:
• AXIS DEER • BROW-ANTLERED DEER • CARIBOU
• CHINESE WATER DEER • FALLOW DEER • MULE DEER
• MUNTJAC • MUSK DEER • PERE DAVID'S DEER
• ROE DEER • SIKA • SOUTH AMERICAN DEER • WAPITI

DEER MOUSE

Dᴇᴇʀ ᴍɪᴄᴇ ᴀʀᴇ ᴠᴇʀʏ sɪᴍɪʟᴀʀ to European wood mice, *Apodemus sylvaticus*, both in appearance and in habits, but the two types of mice belong to different families. There are about 55 species of deer mice, ranging in color from sandy or gray to dark brown. Coat color varies according to a species' natural environment. Some deer mice are almost white and others are nearly black, but in general those living in woods are darkish, and those living in open and arid country are pale. The underparts and feet are white. Deer mice measure 5–15 inches (13–38 cm) from nose to tip of tail. The tail is dark above and white underneath and is 1½–8 inches (4–20 cm) long according to species.

The various species of deer mice range over most of North America, from Alaska and Labrador southward, and one species extends into South America, reaching Colombia. Deer mice inhabit many different kinds of environment from swamps and forests to arid, desertlike country, but each species usually has only a limited habitat and consequently is found only in a relatively small part of the total deer mouse range. The most widespread species is the range deer mouse, *Peromyscus maniculatus*. It is also one of the smallest species.

Overlapping territories

Deer mice are nocturnal, coming out during the day only if they are very hungry or if there is a cover of snow that allows them to forage under its shelter. During the evening they can be heard making a trilling or buzzing sound, a noise quite unlike the squeaks of other mice, and in some parts of the United States this has led to their being called vesper mice. They also drum with the front feet when excited.

Each deer mouse has a home range that it covers regularly in search of food. The extent of the range is ¹⁄₁₀–10 acres (0.04–4 ha), depending on the amount of food available. In the grasslands of southern Michigan, the average size of the ranges of male deer mice is ½ acre (0.2 ha), whereas that of the females is slightly smaller.

In general the home range of a mammal is not strictly comparable to the territory of a bird. Only a few birds keep a territory all through the year and, more significantly, a typical mammal does not defend its range as vigorously as a typical bird. The borders of neighboring ranges overlap, sometimes considerably; indeed the ranges of two females may be almost identical. However, it should be noted that in some cases mammalian and avian territories do perform

Deer mice feed on a wide range of plant matter, including nuts, seeds and berries. They also eat insects and, sometimes, carrion.

very similar functions: they exclude conspecifics (animals of the same species) from important and possibly limited resources, such as food, mates and breeding sites. Deer mice are generally tolerant of conspecifics, though the degree of toleration varies according to species. For example, male California mice, *P. californicus*, are highly aggressive toward one another. Likewise, female white-footed mice, *P. leucopus*, exclude other females from their home ranges.

Within its range, a deer mouse may have several refuges in abandoned bird nests, under logs or in crevices. Sometimes a deer mouse enters a house and makes its nest in an attic or storage room. Nests are used for a short time and abandoned when they become soiled.

Emergency exits

The nest is a mass of grass and leaves, lined with moss, fine grass or feathers. The Oldfield mouse, *P. polionotus*, a species of deer mouse living in Alabama and Florida, makes a tunnel leading down to a nest that is 12 inches (30 cm) underground. From the other side another tunnel leads up again, stopping just short of the surface. Scientists believe that this serves as a bolt-hole in case a snake or another narrow-bodied predator invades the burrow.

Up to nine young may be born in one litter. At birth deer mice are blind, deaf and naked apart from their whiskers.

Deer mice

Seeds and berries are the main food of deer mice but they also eat many insects such as beetles, moths and grasshoppers, which they chase and bite or beat to death. Deer mice also eat insect larvae, snails and slugs and carrion such as dead birds and mammals. They also gnaw antlers that have been shed by deer.

Deer mice are something of a problem in plantations and on farms, where they eat seeds of newly sown crops, which they smell out and dig up. Even when abundant, however, they are not as much of a pest as meadow voles (*Microtus* spp.) and other small rodents. Indeed, they are helpful to farmers in that they they eat chafer grubs, which damage the roots of young trees.

Hanging on to mother

In spring the males search for mates, perhaps finding females with ranges that overlap their own. At first their advances are usually repulsed but the males eventually move into the females' nests. They generally stay there for only a few days but sometimes form permanent pairs.

The female gives birth to a litter of one to nine young after 3–4 weeks. At birth the young mice are blind, deaf and naked, apart from their whiskers. They hang firmly to their mother's teats and she is able to walk around with them trailing behind. If the nest is disturbed, she will drag them in this manner to a new site. Any baby that does fall off is picked up and carried in its mother's mouth. In many species both females and males cooperate in raising the young and remain in largely monogamous family groups.

Litters of deer mice are produced from spring to fall but more young are born in spring and fall than during the summer. If the winter is mild, the deer mice continue to breed through the season. Females begin breeding at 7 weeks, only a few weeks after leaving their mothers, and may produce up to four litters a year.

Most deer mice live less than two years, and many never reach maturity but are killed by the many predators that hunt at night. Foxes, weasels, coyotes, bobcats, owls and snakes all feed on deer mice, and even shrews will occasionally eat them.

Differentiation between species

Although scientists know of 55 species of deer mice other subdivisions may exist; it is not easy for even a specialist to distinguish between them. This might imply that there would be mixing and interbreeding between species and a gradual evening out of the differences between species. However, this has not proved to be the case. Experiments by an American scientist using deer mice from closely related species offered one theory as to how deer mice forms remain distinct.

Special cages were constructed, each with two side compartments. In preparation for the experiment, a Rocky Mountain mouse was put in one compartment and a Florida mouse, *P. floridanus*, in the other. This procedure was repeated in all the cages. After the mice had remained long enough to impart their smell to the compartments they were taken out. The scientist then placed two different mice into the cages, one from each species. These mice made full use of the available space in the cages, and wandered freely into each compartment.

By timing the period each mouse spent in each of the two side compartments of its cage, the scientist found that in all cases the test mouse was very obviously attracted to the compartment that carried the smell of its own species. This almost certainly explains why deer mice of the same species are drawn together to breed, even when they share a habitat with deer mice from another species. Moreover, the results of the experiment suggested that males reacted particularly strongly to the smell of females of their own species in heat.

It would seem that although different species of deer mice do live together and compete for similar resources, their acute sense of smell enables them to distinguish their own species and prevents interbreeding.

Deer mice have large eyes and ears and a long tail. Individual species are difficult to distinguish and often a species' range provides the only means of separation.

DESERT

Lack of fresh water and extremes of temperature make the desert biome one of the harshest environments on earth. However, most deserts are home to diverse communities of specialized plants and animals.

DESERTS COVER ONE-SEVENTH of the earth's land surface. They are formed in several ways, but all of them have one feature in common: they are extremely arid (dry). Any area of land that receives less than 10 inches (25 cm) of rainfall per year is classified as a desert. However, most deserts receive far less than this and in some desert locations it does not rain for decades at a time.

The extreme aridity of the desert biome makes it one of the earth's harshest environments for wildlife. Intricate foodwebs including a variety of plants and animals are nevertheless present, despite the severe conditions.

Creation of tropical deserts
Deserts are common in the areas of land that straddle the tropics of Cancer and Capricorn due to a global climatic phenomenon that causes very low rainfall in these regions. The air near the equator is warm and moist as a result of the intense sunlight and the resultant rapid rate of evaporation from nearby oceans. Warm air rises, and as it does so it cools; when air cools, it cannot hold as much water vapor and releases the excess as precipitation, usually in the form of rain. It follows that as the warm, moist air from equatorial regions rises, it sheds its excess water as rain, giving rise to lush equatorial rain forests. This air becomes relatively cool and dry in the process, and spreads north and south as wind. The cool air starts to sink, heating up once more as it does so. By the time the airflow reaches the Tropics, it has turned into a very hot, dry wind that rarely brings rain. The end result is vast tropical deserts, such as the Kalahari in southern Africa and the deserts of the Australian interior.

Inland and coastal deserts
Outside the Tropics, landlocked areas (land far from the ocean) may also become desert if the winds that reach the region have already lost all of their water vapor. The Takla Makan in northern China is an example of this type of desert.

Some deserts, such as the Atacama Desert in Chile, are on the coast. These deserts are usually situated on the west-facing coasts of tropical landmasses. The ocean currents that flow past western coastlines emanate from the poles and the cold water that they contain cools the air

DESERT

CLIMATE
Very arid, typically with large temperature differential between day and night. Annual rainfall: less than 10 in. (25 cm); maximum temperature: over 104° F (40° C); minimum temperature: about -40° F (-40° C).

VEGETATION
Mainly grasses, dwarf shrubs, cacti and succulents; trees scarce but dominant species include acacias and tamarisks

LOCATION
Largest deserts: Mojave, Sonoran, Great Basin and Chihuahuan (southwestern U.S. and northern Mexico); Atacama (coastal Peru and Chile); Sahara (northern Africa); Kalahari and Namib (southwestern Africa); Arabian (Middle East); Takla Makan and Gobi (Central Asia); Great Sandy, Gibson, Great Victoria and Simpson (inland Australia)

STATUS
Desertification accelerating in many areas, due mainly to overgrazing by cattle, deforestation and global climate change

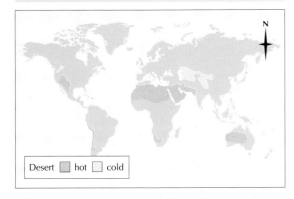

Desert ▨ hot ☐ cold

above, inhibiting the creation of rain clouds. Therefore, rain-bearing winds rarely blow onto western tropical coasts, resulting in the formation of coastal deserts. However, coastal deserts occasionally do receive moisture as fog and during storms.

The Sahara Desert is produced by all of the phenomena described so far and is consequently the largest single desert in the world. It covers 3,320,000 square miles (8,600,000 sq km). Moreover, several other desert areas combine with the Sahara to make an immense, arid zone of sand and rock that stretches from Morocco, west through North Africa, Arabia and Iran to India.

The rain shadow effect

The North American deserts and the massive Gobi Desert of Mongolia are formed by a different phenomenon, known as the rain shadow effect. These regions owe their extreme aridity to nearby mountain ranges, which force winds upward, making the air cool down and shed its water vapor. By the time it reaches the other side of the high ground the air is completely dry. The Cascades and Rocky Mountains dry out the prevailing winds in this way, creating the desert areas of Utah, Nevada and Arizona.

Climate

Deserts are classified as either hot or cold. Tropical deserts are hot: the daytime air temperature usually exceeds 104° F (40° C). An air temperature of 136° F (58° C) has been recorded in the Sahara Desert in Libya, but the ground itself can become even hotter than this: up to 172° F (78° C) in certain parts of the Sahara.

Temperate deserts, such as the Great Basin Desert in Nevada, are cold, and some of them may be extremely cold. The Gobi Desert, for

Solifugids are found in the deserts of Africa, Arabia, southern Asia and the Americas. These active predators are related to spiders and have the strongest jaws relative to body size of any animal.

663

The moloch, or thorny devil, is a common resident of Australian deserts. Lizards and snakes play a vital role in many desert food chains.

instance, is sometimes as cold as -40° F (-40° C). In winter the Gobi receives violent winds and severe blizzards, and average daytime temperatures may remain below freezing for up to 6 months of the year.

Another characteristic of deserts is very large daily temperature fluctuations. Deserts lack rain clouds, which retain a blanket of warm air near the ground. After sunset desert air cools rapidly by as much as 72° F (40° C).

Physical features

Deserts share many physical features. Contrary to popular opinion, most of them are not covered in sand dunes: wind-blown sand represents just 2 percent of the surface of North American deserts and accounts for no more than 10 percent of the Sahara. Generally, deserts are broad plains of rock, gravel and sand interrupted only by steep valleys and heavily weathered mountains. Winds transport clouds of dust and drive large volumes of sand particles across the ground.

A desert is a stressful environment for plants. Desert soil is immature, which is to say that it contains very little organic matter. It is therefore unable to nourish the roots of most plants. In addition, when rain finally comes, the coarse, sandy soil can retain only tiny amounts of water. Strong winds blow the topsoil away, disturbing root systems and enabling precious nutrients to leach away. However, big communities of microorganisms exist in the soil.

Desert plants

Plants survive the harsh conditions of the desert biome in a number of ways. Some perennial plants—ones that live and reproduce for years—are adapted to absorb moisture through their leaves and stems. When water vapor is unavailable, these parts of the plants dry out and wither, only to be reinvigorated by the next shower, perhaps years later. Other species of perennials survive by growing food reserves underground, often in the form of bulbs, while the rest of the plant dies back. When the bulbs at last receive moisture, they quickly sprout, flower and produce seeds before the soil dries out again.

Annual plants, which die soon after reproducing for the first time, have an alternative strategy for survival in deserts. They produce hardy seeds that can lie dormant in the soil for decades, but which can grow and reproduce in a matter of weeks when rain comes. These are the plants that cause a desert to bloom after a rainstorm.

Some desert plants do not have to wait for water. Cacti and succulents retain a supply of water in their fleshy stems, and their specialized leaves minimize water loss by evaporation. The leaves either have become spines or have evolved a waxy and hairy surface. Trees are scarce in deserts, although a few species, such as acacias and tamarisks, are widespread.

Shrubs and grasses are the most common desert plants, especially in temperate regions. Members of the saltbush family are found in deserts across Africa and Asia. A few species are associated with a single desert. For example, the joshua tree, *Yucca bevifolia*, is found only in the Mojave Desert, California.

Desert animals

The animal populations of deserts are more regionally distinct than their plant communities. This is largely because animals cannot easily migrate between desert areas, whereas the seeds of plants can be spread by the wind. Australian deserts, for instance, are notable because the available ecological niches are filled with fewer mammals and more reptiles than is the case in deserts elsewhere. Among the many reptiles native to Australian deserts are the moloch (*Moloch horridus*), the bearded lizards (genus *Pogona*) and the taipan (*Oxyuranus microlepidotus*), one of the most venomous of all snakes.

A typical desert "comes alive" at nightfall. Most of the small mammals, reptiles and insects that inhabit deserts forage in the cool of the night in order to conserve water, which would be lost at an excessive rate during the heat of the day. They take to their burrows by day to shelter from the strong sunlight and hot air. Small desert residents include the gerbils (family Cricetidae) and jerboas (family Dipodidae) of Africa and Asia, the pocket mice (genus *Perognathus*) and kangaroo rats (genus *Dipodomys*) of North America and a variety of scorpions, spiders and beetles.

Large desert mammals are less at risk from water loss as the ratio between their body weight and the surface area of their body is significantly smaller. Even so, they have had to evolve sophisticated methods of thermoregulation to enable them to keep cool while feeding out in the open. These mammals are relatively few in number but include the two species of camels (genus *Camelus*), the Saharan addax (*Addax nasomaculatus*) and the four species of oryxes (genus *Oryx*) of Africa and the Middle East. The bat-eared fox, *Otocyon megalotis*, and fennec fox, *Fennecus zerda*, have proportionately huge ears that act as radiators.

Desert birds tend to live a nomadic lifestyle, flying between areas that have had recent rain. Birds of prey and carrion-eating species can obtain all the water they require from their food,

but seed-eating birds such as sandgrouse, parrots and finches must search for surface water to drink. Large flocks of sandgrouse fly to waterholes every day, and in each locality they follow an established route and timetable.

Many desert reptiles estivate (become dormant) during prolonged dry periods. For example, *Cyclorana alboguttatus*, a frog from western Australia, secretes a sheath around its body that retains moisture while it lies dormant underground. It emerges after the next rains.

Conservation

Desertification is now a major problem in many regions. As a result of this process existing deserts increase in size, and fertile land gradually becomes more arid and desertlike until it has turned into an entirely new expanse of desert. One of the main causes of desertification is thought to be the introduction of excessive numbers of domestic animals, especially donkeys and goats, to semiarid grasslands. The animals' hooves compact the already fragile soil and prevent the growth of plant roots. This creates an arid dust bowl in which even desert-specialized plants are unable to survive.

Deserts may appear to be devoid of wildlife, but this is usually an illusion. Most desert animals are nocturnal or nomadic, and as a result are rarely seen by humans.

DESMAN

This is the Pyrenean desman. A desman must regularly groom in order to spread oils through the coat and keep it waterproof.

DESMANS ARE AMPHIBIOUS mammals of the same family as moles, having the flexible snout and small eyes typical of moles and shrews. Often all that is seen of a desman is its long snout showing above water as it swims. The scaly tail is long, equal to the head and body length, and flattened from side to side. Along the length of the tail is a ridge of hairs, which increase its efficiency as a propeller. Desmans swim with a side-to-side motion of the tail, helped by their hind feet, which are webbed with stiff hairs bordering the outside toes, providing a larger area with which to paddle the water. The front feet are also fringed with hair but are only partly webbed. Desmans are primarily nocturnal creatures. Their eyes are not large, but they have an excellent sense of smell and touch that they use to orient themselves and to find prey.

The Russian desman, *Desmana moschata*, is the largest member of the family Talpidae and is the best known of the two desman species. It now lives in the river basins of the Ural, Kama, Volga and Don, and in small rivers flowing into the Sea of Azov. It is found in the slower-running parts of the rivers and in lakes and pools such as swampy oxbow pools formed where the rivers have changed course. The Pyrenean desman, *Galemys pyrenaicus*, prefers faster-flowing streams and occurs in northern Spain and Portugal and in the southern borders of France. Research suggests that this species may use echolocation to find its way around its home territory. Pyrenean and Russian desmans are very similar and fossil records suggest that the current populations are the descendants of desmans that once ranged across Europe, including the British Isles.

Underwater runways

Russian desmans live in burrows, emerging to feed at night, whereas Pyrenean desmans only rarely dig their own burrows. Instead, they shelter in water vole burrows, rock crevices and caves. The burrows of Russian desmans are dug in the banks of rivers and pools and lead to nest cavities just under the surface of the ground, usually beneath a log or boulder or among the roots of a bush. Because the nest is near the surface, it is ventilated by air filtering down through the soil, while the log, boulder or bush protects the roof of the nest from being damaged by the weight of larger animals. In winter, such protection also prevents snow from blanketing the burrow and cutting off the air supply.

The burrow leads from the nest to the water, opening well under the surface, so the entrance is not blocked by ice in winter. The length of the burrow depends on the slope of the bank; it is short if the bank is steep and long if the bank gently shelves to the water's edge. The nest is built above the normal water level but it may be flooded in spring, when the desmans have to flee to higher ground and make temporary nests. Desman populations often move location due to water level changes. Sometimes, the floods come before the ice has melted and the desmans are trapped. Populations have been wiped out in areas where ice has persisted in the spring floods.

If a burrow is occupied, there is often a litter of fish bones at the entrance, and a clear channel leading to it through the bed of the river or pool. A musky odor produced by scent glands at the base of the desman's tail is also a characteristic of its burrow. If debris has lodged in the channel, it means that the burrow is abandoned, for desmans are very much creatures of habit and have runways or trenches leading from their burrows and through the shallows, which they use as regularly as a mole uses its tunnels.

DESMANS

CLASS **Mammalia**

ORDER **Insectivora**

FAMILY **Talpidae**

GENUS AND SPECIES **Russian desman,**
Desmana moschata; **Pyrenean desman,**
Galenys pyrenaicus

LENGTH
**Russian desman, head and body:
7–8½ in. (18–22 cm); tail: 6½–8½ in.
(17–21.5 cm). Pyrenean desman,
head and body: 4⅓–6⅓ in. (11–16 cm);
tail: 4¾–6⅓ in. (12–16 cm).**

DISTINCTIVE FEATURES
**Long, flexible snout; broad forepaws;
webbed digits; small eyes and ears; long,
flattened scaly tail with ridge of hairs**

DIET
**Aquatic insects and larvae, crustaceans,
snails, leeches, worms, frogs and fish**

BREEDING
**Breeding season: January–May; number of
young: usually 1 to 5; gestation period:
about 30 days; breeding interval: 2 litters
per year (Russian desman)**

LIFE SPAN
Up to 4 years

HABITAT
**Freshwater streams and lakes; Russian
desman also in ponds; Pyrenean desman
prefers fast-flowing streams in mountains**

DISTRIBUTION
**Russian desman: western Russia in Volga,
Kama, Don and Ural River Basins; Belarus
and Ukraine. Pyrenean desman: northern
Spain and Portugal; south of France in
Pyrenees Mountains.**

STATUS
Both species vulnerable

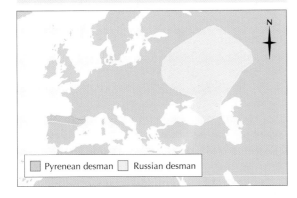

Pyrenean desman □ Russian desman

Active predators

Like moles, shrews and hedgehogs, desmans are active, voracious predators. They eat small freshwater animals: crustaceans, snails, insect larvae, leeches, worms, frogs and fish. The Pyrenean desman also hunts on land, searching for insects among the vegetation on the banks. Its mainstay is freshwater amphipods (small crustaceans) and it will eat both live prey and carrion.

Desmans are eaten by birds of prey such as ospreys, kites and harriers. They are also thought to be preyed on by mammals and large fish.

Obscure breeding habits

Little is known about the breeding habits of desmans and, considering their underground and underwater life, it would be very difficult to make a study of courtship and care of the young. Pyrenean desmans reach sexual maturity in the second year of life. The mating season is known to run from January to May in the Pyrenees, and is probably the same in Russia. There are one to five young, occasionally more. Judging by related insectivorous mammals, it is unlikely that the male plays any part in raising the family.

The lure of the fur

Desman populations were severely reduced in the late 19th century, when the animals were hunted for their soft, molelike, reddish fur and for their musk glands, which were used in the manufacture of perfumes. Habitat destruction, water pollution and competition for food and nesting sites from introduced species such as the coypu or nutria, *Myocastor coypus*, and the muskrat, *Ondatra zibethicus*, have also affected desman numbers. The Russian authorities subsequently took measures to conserve the species and to introduce them to new areas, such as the basin of the Dnieper River. Russian desmans are now an officially protected species. Pyrenean desmans are currently regarded as vulnerable, due to the destruction of their habitat.

*Russian desmans have
two layers to their fur:
a short inner layer and
a longer, stiff outer
layer. These offer
vital insulation in the
cold freshwater lakes,
ponds and streams that
the animals inhabit.*

DEVILFISH

Devilfish propel themselves by strokes of their enormous pectoral fins, which have become modified into underwater wings.

FEWER THAN 15 SPECIES of devilfish are known. They are divided into two genera, *Manta* and *Mobula*, both of which belong to the family Myliobatidae. Devilfish are related to skates, rays and sharks, and like them have a cartilaginous skeleton. The largest species is the Atlantic manta ray or greater devilfish, *Manta birostris*, which grows to a width of about 22 feet (6.7 m) and may weigh as much as 3,500 pounds (1,600 kg). The smallest species is the pygmy Australian devil ray, *Mobula diabolis*, which is only 8 feet (2.4 m) across.

Other, unrelated species known as devilfish include those of the genus *Synanceia*, inhabitants of shallow water and coral that are usually called stonefish. The genus *Paraplesiops* also contains several fish that bear the name, including the southern blue devilfish, *P. meleagris*, which is found in the seas around Australia.

Manta and Mobula

Members of the genus *Manta* are commonly referred to as manta rays. The genus *Mobula* contains smaller, bottom-living species known as

devil rays. *Manta* means "blanket" in Spanish and refers to the shape of the pectoral fins. The Atlantic manta ray, Pacific manta ray, (*M. hamiltoni*) and Prince Alfred's manta ray (*M. alfredi*) are three of the most common species. As in other rays, the body of a manta ray is flattened from above downward, and the pectoral fins are large and triangular. The tail is long and slender and some species have a small poison spine. In the related stingrays the spine is large.

Species in the genus *Manta* have a terminal mouth at the front of the head, and have teeth in only the lower jaw. Members of the genus *Mobula* are almost flat and have a ventral mouth, which is situated on the underside of the body, and teeth in both the upper and the lower jaws. At each corner of the mouth is a large, forward-facing movable lobe, a part of the pectoral fin known as the cephalic fin. The hornlike shape of the cephalic fins has given rise to the species' common name of devilfish. Members of this group are the only living vertebrates with three pairs of functional limbs: small pelvic fins, large pectoral fins and smaller cephalic fins. The

DEVILFISH

CLASS	**Chondrichthyes**
ORDER	**Rajiformes**
FAMILY	**Myliobatidae**
GENUS	***Manta* and *Mobula***
SPECIES	**13, including *Manta birostris*; *Manta hamiltoni*; and *Mobula diabolis***

ALTERNATIVE NAMES
***Manta*: manta ray; *Mobula*: devil ray**

WEIGHT
Up to 3,500 lb. (1,600 kg)

LENGTH
Across wings: 8–22 ft. (2.4–6.7 m)

DISTINCTIVE FEATURES
Wide, disc-shaped body; large, roughly triangular wings (pectoral fins) with convex front edge and concave rear edge; small pelvic fins; hornlike lobe at each corner of mouth; slender tail; color of upperparts variable, lower surface white

DIET
Plankton, crustaceans and small fish

BREEDING
Age at first breeding: when 16 ft. (5 m) wide (female); breeding season: probably all year; number of young: 1 or 2

LIFE SPAN
Not known

HABITAT
Tropical and warm temperate seas

DISTRIBUTION
***Manta*: circumtropical range, usually between 35° N and 35° S. *Mobula*: Indian Ocean and western Pacific, north to Japan and south to South Africa and Australia.**

STATUS
Some species common; others uncommon

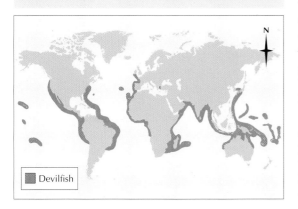

Devilfish

coloration of devilfish is variable. The upperparts may be black, grayish blue, reddish brown or green, while the underside is often pure white.

Devilfish are mostly found in the warm waters around islands and continents. Manta rays have a wide circumtropical range although some species, such as Prince Alfred's manta ray and the Japanese manta ray, *Manta japonicus*, have a more restricted distribution. In general manta rays favor the open ocean, though they sometimes pass over coral reefs.

Surface-dwelling fish

Unlike other rays and skates, which live mainly on the seabed, manta rays spend most of their time swimming at or near the surface. They swim with graceful, flapping movements of the enormous pectoral fins, as if flying through the water. The unusual size and shape of these fins gives manta rays the appearance of underwater bats. For this reason they were once called sea bats and vampire rays.

Devilfish sometimes form small schools although they are more usually found alone or in pairs. Normally they swim slowly. However, at times devilfish turn complete somersaults, or leap high into the air, landing in the water with a tremendous impact.

Devilfish feed by swimming through shoals of plankton or small fish with their large mouths open. Manta *species spend most of their time near the water surface, where the populations of their preferred prey are highest.*

The Atlantic manta ray is the largest species of devilfish. It may measure 22 feet (6.7 m) across.

Large fish, small food

When cruising through water rich in plankton, a devilfish feeds by using its horns like scoops to fan food toward its enormous mouth. One reason for turning somersaults in the water is to take advantage of a particularly rich source of plankton. By swimming round and round, the devilfish creates strong currents that help it to feed. A special latticework covering the gills keeps the food in the mouth until it can be swallowed. Without this, the gills would become clogged. Devilfish also feed on small crustaceans and young or very small fish. They feed on small fish by swimming through a shoal with their mouths gaping wide open, swallowing as many fish as they can.

Manta rays are frequently accompanied by pilot fish (family Carangidae) and remoras (family Echeneidae). When the manta ray feeds, these smaller fish dart out to take the scraps of food that their large host leaves. Scientists believe that they also feed on parasites carried by the manta ray. This is an example of a symbiotic relationship (relationship of mutual benefit).

Outsize young

Devilfish are ovoviviparous, producing eggs that develop within the mother's body and hatch almost immediately after being extruded. Sexual maturity is probably reached when the span of the pectoral fins reaches about 16 feet (5 m). There is no evidence that devilfish have a specific breeding season, and experts presume that mating occurs throughout the year. Devilfish breed in fairly shallow waters. The two partners come together, their undersides facing, the female curving her pectoral fins upward to embrace those of the male. The male possesses a pair of organs, known as claspers, which are used alternately to insert sperm into the female's oviduct. Usually there are only one or two young at birth, known as pups. These are well-developed and large and are born wrapped up in their wing flaps. One female that measured 15 feet (4.5 feet) across contained an embryo 5 feet (1.5 m) wide, weighing 20 pounds (9 kg).

Myth of the devilfish

For many years tradition held that devilfish were capable of smothering pearl divers with their large wings and devouring them. Sailors also believed that devilfish could seize an anchor and tow a vessel away. It is likely that three factors, in addition to the large size of the devilfish, contributed toward these beliefs. Certainly a manta ray can be inadvertently dangerous to a small boat by smashing or capsizing it with a blow of its pectoral fins; it may also accidentally strike a boat following a leap. It is also true that a harpooned manta ray can tow a reasonably large vessel. Moreover, the noise that the fish can make when landing after a leap may have contributed to the idea of the devilfish as a destructive animal. However, devilfish are harmless.

DHOLE

THE DHOLE, ALSO CALLED the red, or wild, dog of India and Southeast Asia, resembles village or pi-dogs, with which it is sometimes confused. It is distinguished from them by its rounded ears and shorter muzzle. In the northern parts of its range the dhole has a heavy, yellowish to grayish brown coat with dense underfur in winter, turning darker in summer. To the south, the coat is thinner and is yellowish brown all year. The tail is tipped with black.

The dhole's range covers India and Southeast Asia to Indonesia, as well as parts of the former Soviet Union, south Mongolia, China and Korea. It favors tropical or subtropical mountains and forests, grassland and scrub, and is found at altitudes of up to 13,100 feet (4,000 m).

In India dholes are born year-round, though mostly in January and February. After a gestation of about 9 weeks, two to six young are born. Several females may raise their young in a communal den, and there may be several dens in one territory. Mother and offspring are fed with regurgitated meat by other pack members. The young join in kills when they are 70–80 days old.

Roam in packs

Dholes are social animals and once lived in packs of 100 or more on forested hillsides and plains. Their numbers are now decreasing because the deer and other mammals on which they feed have become scarce. A pack might now typically consist of 5 to 20 dogs.

Packs are extended family groups, consisting of a pair of dholes and their young. Larger groups are thought to be made up of a combination of several family units. In the past dhole packs would remain in one area, sheltering under boulders or in deserted burrows and hunting by day until they had killed so much game that they were forced to move on to a new area. Now that numbers of muntjac, chital and other deer are depleted, dholes are often shot to prevent the surviving herds of deer from being completely destroyed.

Tireless hunters

Dholes growl and whine but do not bark. Hunters are able to decoy them by blowing across a brass cartridge case to imitate their peculiar howling whistle. Like the Cape hunting dogs of Africa, to which they are related, dholes hunt in packs. When they are hunting in forest, dholes use their distinctive shrill call to communicate with each other and to co-ordinate the pursuit of their prey. They do not run at any great speed but follow the scent of their prey in a long, loping, tireless canter until the victim is eventually worn down and may be attacked.

Dholes share the meat of a kill and only very rarely fight over it. Young pack members are often allowed to feed first.

671

DHOLE

CLASS	**Mammalia**
ORDER	**Carnivora**
FAMILY	**Canidae**
GENUS AND SPECIES	*Cuon alpinus*

ALTERNATIVE NAMES
Wild dog; Asiatic wild dog; red wolf; red dog; chennai

WEIGHT
33–44 lb. (15–20 kg)

LENGTH
Head and body: 31–45 in. (80–115 cm); shoulder height: 16–21 in. (42–55 cm); tail: 15½–19½ in. (40–50 cm)

DISTINCTIVE FEATURES
Long, slender legs; relatively short tail; rounded ears; yellowish or brownish coat, often with darker tail

DIET
Mainly small and medium-sized mammals, especially deer, sheep, goats, hares, rabbits and rodents; also birds, insects, carrion and some vegetable matter

BREEDING
Age at first breeding: probably 2–3 years; breeding season: all year; number of young: up to 6; gestation period: usually 60–63 days; breeding interval: 1 year

LIFE SPAN
Up to 15 years in captivity

HABITAT
Varied, includes forest, scrub jungle, arid scrub plains and alpine zones of mountains

DISTRIBUTION
Southern Russia and Mongolia south through China and India to Indonesia

STATUS
Vulnerable

Dholes are mainly forest animals. Their distinctive call enables a pack to communicate during a chase when dense vegetation makes visual contact impossible.

Once within striking distance of the exhausted prey, the dholes attack any part that can be grasped, slashing the flanks and hanging on to the lips, nose or tail. It seems that dholes do not attack any part of the body in particular, but seize any part they can. Dholes will occasionally scavenge or take carrion if they have no alternative food source. They also eat some vegetable matter, insects and fruit.

Muntjac, chital or axis deer and sambar are the main prey of dholes in India, but the packs will attack larger animals, including Indian or water buffalo, wild boars and even other carnivores such as Asiatic black bears and sloth bears. Tigers and leopards take flight after a clash with a pack of dholes, perhaps over the ownership of a kill, and they are frequently forced to take to the trees. If caught, the pack can overwhelm and kill individual big cats. Dholes are voracious feeders and an individual animal may eat almost 11 pounds (5 kg) of meat in an hour.

Although dholes readily attack deer they play a useful part in the overall balance of nature. They keep the deer moving and control their populations, and in this way prevent them from overgrazing the land.

Villagers may benefit from the dholes' activities, obtaining meat by following a pack and driving the dogs off the kill. However, dholes compete with hunters for prey and kill livestock. As a result they are regarded as a pest by farmers and some governments issue bounties for them. Consequently dholes are persecuted and have become rare outside protected areas, such as wildlife reservations.

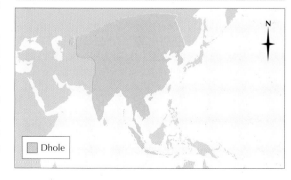

☐ Dhole

DIBATAG

The dibatag is similar in appearance to another African antelope, the gerenuk. It is distinguishable from the latter by its habit of holding its head and tail erect in flight.

THE DIBATAG IS A long-necked gazellelike antelope, also known as Clarke's gazelle. It was not discovered until 1891 and has been seen only intermittently since then, although it can be numerous locally. The male stands 30–35 inches (75–90 cm) at the shoulder, and weighs up to 75 pounds (34 kg). Its coat is grayish fawn on the upperparts and white on the belly. There is a white streak on each side of the face ending in a whitish ring around each eye. The ears are long and tipped with black. The tail is 12 inches (30 cm) or more in length and is mainly black. The muzzle is hairy and very delicate, as are the highly mobile lips. Consequently, when two males fight each other, they keep their vulnerable mouthparts tucked down by their forefeet to minimize the risk of damage from the opponent's sharp horns.

When it is fleeing from danger, the dibatag carries its neck and tail erect. As the animal runs, its neck moves backward and its tail moves forward. This characteristic gait has given rise to its name, which derives from the Somali for tail, *dabu,* and erect, *tag,* and distinguishes the dibatag from the gerenuk, or Waller's gazelle, which carries its tail horizontally in flight. Only the male dibatag has horns; these may grow to 13 inches (33 cm) long, and curve backward, then forward and slightly outward.

A restricted range

The dibatag seems to have a well-defined home range, though it moves from one area to another during different seasons. Its movements are probably dependent on which plants are in leaf. The dibatag feeds primarily on the foliage of evergreen trees and shrubs, grazing also on herbs and new grass in the rainy season. Although usually limited to bushland and thicket, the dibatag's range extends to more open glades immediately after the rains. The species keeps mainly to durr grass on open grassy plains with scattered small scrubby bushes and umbrella mimosa. The dibatag's reliance on a particular vegetation type restricts it to central Somalia and eastern Ethiopia.

Shy and well-camouflaged

Knowledge of the dibatag's habits is limited because the animal is rare and hard to see. Its color makes it inconspicuous and it generally stays near or within cover. Durr grass often grows up to 6 feet (1.8 m) tall and may therefore completely hide the 4-feet high (1.2-m) dibatag. The dibatag's shyness and alert senses make it impossible to approach the animal to within a range of 100 yards (90 m) except when in the open, when it seems to be less wary and can be approached to about 50 yards (45 m). When resting, the dibatag usually lies in a slight depression in the ground or in the lee (sheltered side) of a bush.

Dibatags feed in the morning and late afternoon, keeping to the shade of a bush or tree during the midday heat. They feed on durr grass but seem to prefer the leaves and flowers of acacia and the leaves of the *Commiphora* shrub. Dibatags have pointed, muscular lips that enable them to pluck small buds and shoots from thorny brush. Like the long-necked gerenuks, dibatags sometimes stand on their hind legs with the forefeet planted against the trunk of the tree when browsing. Few other scrubland animals are capable of reaching vegetation that grows above ground level in this way, and this helps to limit competition for food. However, dibitags are less skillful than gerenuks in this manner of feeding and employ it only occasionally.

Young concealed in a bush

The dibatag lives in pairs, in groups of three to five or in small family groups of up to seven in areas that are hot throughout the year and fairly dry. Breeding appears to take place throughout the year but there is a main breeding season in March–May that coincides with the rainy season. There is one young per birth, which the mother leaves concealed in a convenient bush for up to 2 weeks. She returns from time to time during this period to nurse her offspring until it is strong enough to follow her.

Dibatags are preyed upon by hyenas, wild dogs, lions, leopards, cheetahs and some of the smaller cats, such as caracals. Their main weapon against predators is their natural wariness. Though dibatags are a vulnerable species, illegal hunting and the destruction of their natural habitat to create land for raising livestock persists. Dibatags inhabit a restricted area that is being encroached upon by humans. A civil war in this region of Africa has also been severely detrimental to their environment. It is these factors, rather than the actions of natural predators in the wild, that has caused dibatag numbers to fall steeply. Current estimates place the dibatag population in the wild at 5,000 to 10,000.

DIBATAG

CLASS	**Mammalia**
ORDER	**Artiodactyla**
FAMILY	**Bovidae**
GENUS AND SPECIES	***Ammodorcas clarkei***

ALTERNATIVE NAME
Clarke's gazelle

WEIGHT
60–75 lb. (27–34 kg)

LENGTH
Head and body: 4 ft. (1.2 m); shoulder height: 29–35 in. (74–90 cm); tail: about 14 in. (35.5 cm)

DISTINCTIVE FEATURES
Slender build; long legs; long neck; long tail, held upright when fleeing; mainly grayish fawn coat with reddish forehead and white underparts; short, forward curving horns with annulated (ringed) bases; prominent, pointed ears

DIET
Desert and scrub vegetation, especially foliage of evergreen trees and shrubs

BREEDING
Age at first breeding: 12–18 months; breeding season: probably all year with peak in March–May; number of young: probably 1; gestation period: about 200 days

LIFE SPAN
Probably up to 12 years

HABITAT
Sandy areas in thorny bush and thickets

DISTRIBUTION
Eastern Ethiopia (Ogaden region) and adjoining parts of central Somalia

STATUS
Vulnerable; estimated population: 5,000 to 10,000

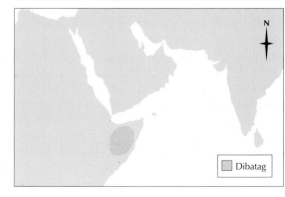

Dibatag

DIK–DIK

IK-DIKS ARE SMALL ANTELOPES that range over Africa south and east of the Sahara. The distribution of dik-diks gives some indication as to how they evolved. Three of the four species occur in the Horn of Africa, to the northeast of the continent, where the group probably originated. The most primitive species, Salt's dik-dik, *Madoqua saltiana*, is least able to tolerate high heat. Consequently, it is primarily nocturnal and inhabits evergreen thickets on the high plateau of Ethiopia. The long-nosed Guenther's dik-dik, *M. guentheri*, is more advanced, and more able to stand high temperatures. It lives in deserts and semideserts and is more diurnal in lifestyle.

The first species of dik-dik that Europeans became aware of, in 1816, was Salt's dik-dik. The species was named after Sir Henry Salt, an explorer who traveled widely in northwestern Africa, especially Abyssinia (present-day Ethiopia), in the early 19th century.

Dik-diks are named for the alarm call of the female, which is variously transcribed as *zik-zik* and *dik-dik*. In addition both sexes produce a shrill whistling sound. The calls of these small antelopes alert a variety of other animals to any disturbance in the locality. Consequently, hunters regard dik-diks as a nuisance and have killed great numbers in the past in order to prevent them from scaring off game animals.

Dik-diks are 19½–27½ inches (50–70 cm) long, stand 12–15¾ inches (30–40 cm) at the shoulder and weigh 6½–15½ pounds (3–7 kg). The females are larger than the males. Their coat is soft, gray to red brown and gray to white on the underparts. Only the males have horns. These are short and stout at the base, ringed and longitudinally grooved, and often partly hidden in a tuft of hair on the top of the head. Both sexes have a pair of crescent-shaped scent glands on the face in front of the eyes. The tail is short. Other features include a hairy muzzle and longish snout.

Harelike antelopes

Dik-diks are shy and elusive animals. They readily disappear into cover, but if flushed out they race away with erratic leaps, somewhat in the manner of hares, on a more or less zigzag course. They live solitarily or in pairs, although occasionally they gather together in small family groups. Where there are dense thorn thickets, dik-diks may gather in larger numbers, but they

The large eyes of dik-diks are an adaptation to feeding in the half-light of evening. Kirk's dik-dik (above) is sometimes also active by day.

In Guenther's dik-dik the nose is enlarged into a proboscis. This species inhabits hot, arid habitats and the elaborate nose helps it to regulate its body temperature.

usually live in dry areas with only scattered brush vegetation. Individuals, pairs and family groups regularly mark the boundaries of their respective territories with dung, urine and face-gland deposits.

Feed at dusk

Most dik-dik species feed mainly at twilight, browsing herbs, shrubs and trees. One analysis of their stomach contents, made in a game park, showed that antelopes had been feeding on 56 percent leaves of shrubs, 23 percent leaves of trees and 17 percent grasses; the remainder of their diet was made up of herbs and sedges. Dik-diks have also been seen eating acacia pods knocked down by feeding vervet monkeys, *Cercopithecus pygerythrus*. Dik-diks use their long, mobile snouts to grasp vegetation. Where there is enough drinking water dik-diks sometimes frequent the banks of streams. In drier areas they seem to obtain sufficient water from their food and from dew to be able to go for months without drinking if necessary.

Secretive lifestyle

Little is known of the mating habits and reproductive cycles of dik-diks. Scientists believe that the young are usually born during and at the end of the rainy season. There is little information on the predators of dik-diks although presumably medium-sized carnivores of all kinds prey on them. Most dik-dik species are not under threat. However, the silver dik-dik, *Madoqua piacentinii*, which is not well adapted to arid conditions and which has a highly restricted range, is hunted with nets. It has no formal protection and the survival of this species is dependent on the maintenance of conservation areas.

DIK–DIKS

CLASS	**Mammalia**
ORDER	**Artiodactyla**
FAMILY	**Bovidae**
GENUS	***Madoqua***

SPECIES **Salt's dik-dik, *M. saltiana*; Kirk's dik-dik, *M. kirkii*; Guenther's dik-dik, *M. guentheri*; silver dik-dik, *M. piacentinii***

WEIGHT
6½–15½ lb. (3–7 kg)

LENGTH
Head and body: 19½–27½ in. (50–70 cm); shoulder height: 12–15¾ in. (30–40 cm); tail: 1⅖–2⅓ in. (3.5–6 cm)

DISTINCTIVE FEATURES
Very small size; slender build; large eyes and ears; crescent-shaped gland in front of each eye; pointed, mobile snout; tuft of hair on head; short, stout horns (male only)

DIET
Shoots, buds and leaves of shrubs, trees and succulents; also grasses, herbs and bark

BREEDING
Age at first breeding: probably 15–18 months; number of young: 1; gestation period: about 170 days; breeding interval: usually 6 months

LIFESPAN
Probably up to 10 years

HABITAT
Scrub, grassland and savanna

DISTRIBUTION
***M. kirkii*: southern Angola and Namibia. Other species: Ethiopia and Somalia south through Kenya to Tanzania.**

STATUS
Generally fairly common; vulnerable: *M. piaceninii*

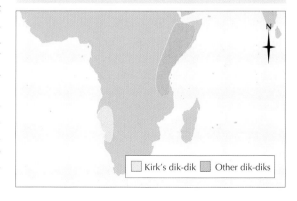

Kirk's dik-dik ☐ Other dik-diks ▨

DINGO

The dingo is the wild dog of Australia. It grows to about the size of a collie and stands approximately 20 inches (50 cm) at the shoulder. Adult dingoes weigh about 33 pounds (15 kg). The ears are erect and pointed; the tail is bushy, often with a white tip, and grows to a length of 10–16 inches (25–40 cm). Dingoes have short coats that vary in color from light red or ginger to brown. Some may be brown with black streaks. The feet and chest are usually white. Albino dingoes are also known and there is a whitish form in southeastern Australia.

The darker dingoes are often assumed to be the offspring of crossbreeding with domestic Alsatians. This is not necessarily so, though crosses between dingoes and domestic dogs are quite common; the male dingo marks its territory with urine, in the way that a domestic dog does. Present-day aboriginal peoples use dingoes for hunting and capture them when young.

The native peoples' companion

Australian mammals are unique to that country. In prehistoric times the continent was cut off from the main landmass that later became Europe, Asia and Africa before the placental, or true, mammals evolved. As a result, the marsupial, pouched mammals were able to survive in large numbers. In the late 18th century, when Europeans first arrived on the continent, the only true mammals apart from humans were bats, rats (scientists believe that the latter floated over from Southeast Asia on driftwood) and dingoes.

Zoologists have found remains of dingoes in Australia dating back 6,000 years. They believe that the dingoes were originally brought over as domestic dogs in one of the invasions of aboriginal peoples from Asia. Some dogs later became feral; these are the ancestors of modern dingoes. As there were no large native carnivores to compete with, the dingoes flourished in the wild and rapidly spread over the continent. The wild dogs in New Guinea are thought to have had the same origin and are known as singing dogs.

Support for this theory lies in the similarity between the dingo and the Asian pariah dogs. They may both have descended from the dhole, *Cuon alpinus*. Neither the dhole, the dingo nor the singing dog can bark. Instead they howl or whine, the howl of the singing dog being a distinctive yodel that gives the dog its name.

The dingo's only early competitors were the Tasmanian devil, *Sarcophilus harrisii*, and the now-extinct Tasmanian wolf or thylacine. It is probably competition with the dingo that caused the Tasmanian devil and the Tasmanian wolf to become rare and finally extinct on the mainland. The dingo never reached Tasmania, and consequently this island is the only area in the region where these two species survived.

Dingoes live alone or in small family parties. They are found all over Australia and seem to make regular migrations along definite tracks. There is evidence that many dingoes breed in inland parts of Australia and move to the coastal strip in winter, where the climate is milder.

Interbreeding between dingoes and domestic dogs is resulting in widespread hybridization. This is the main threat to the species.

677

In Australia, dingoes mainly inhabit scrubland and semidesert regions.

DINGO

CLASS	**Mammalia**
ORDER	**Carnivora**
FAMILY	**Canidae**
GENUS AND SPECIES	***Canis familiaris***

WEIGHT
Up to 48½ lb. (22 kg), usually 33 lb. (15 kg)

LENGTH
Head and body: up to 44 in. (1.1 m); shoulder height: 16–25½ in. (40–65 cm); tail: 10–16 in. (25–40 cm)

DISTINCTIVE FEATURES
Coat short and typically ginger, usually with white patches on chest and feet; white tip to tail; true dingoes have larger canine and carnassial teeth than hybrids with domestic dogs

DIET
Varied and omnivorous, includes kangaroos and other marsupials, rabbits and some domestic stock; also some vegetation and insects

BREEDING
Age at first breeding: 2 years; breeding season: April–May; number of young: usually 3 to 5; gestation period: about 63 days; breeding interval: 1 year

LIFE SPAN
Up to 10 years

HABITAT
Mainly scrub, semidesert and light woodland; also rain forest

DISTRIBUTION
Australia except Tasmania; closely related wild dogs also occur in New Guinea

STATUS
Common. Size of pure population not known due to significant hybridization with domestic dogs.

Dingo

Persistent predators

The size of dingo groups is related to the size of the prey in a particular region. Where only small prey is available, such as rabbits or small marsupials, dingoes hunt as solitary animals, though sometimes they work in pairs. If only large prey is available, dingoes may occasionally band together to hunt cooperatively. Like all dogs, dingoes wear their prey out in a long chase, for they are not fast runners. They relentlessly pursue large animals such as kangaroos, sheep and cattle until the prey tires. If there are a number of sheep or cattle in a group, the dingoes harass them until the weaker ones drop back. As the prey weakens, the dingoes worry at it, slashing at the head and legs but avoiding the hooves, until it collapses and may be attacked. Although they are predominantly carnivorous, dingoes also eat some plant material and insects.

Not all of the dingoes' prey are easily overcome. A kangaroo at bay can be an aggressive adversary. Leaning back on its tail, it is able to deliver kicks powerful enough to rip open the dingoes' bellies. Apart from humans and prey brought to bay, dingoes are vulnerable to attacks

from crocodiles and snakes in the tropical parts of Australia, and from the wedge-tailed eagle, *Aquila audax*. This is one of the world's largest eagles, and two working together have been seen to kill an adult dingo, but this is exceptional. Usually only young or old and infirm dingoes fall prey to the eagles.

Breeding

The dingo mates once a year, unlike the domestic dog which usually breeds biannually. It mates in winter and the pups are born in spring or summer some 9 weeks later. The litter consists of up to eight pups, though three to five is a more usual figure. The pups are sheltered in a den where they are suckled for 2 months and reared by both parents. After this period they stay with their parents for at least a year and hunt as a family group. In areas where large prey is predominant, and dingoes form packs, all adult members of the pack contribute toward the pups' upbringing and care.

Extinction through hybridization?

Since Europeans began farming in Australia, dingoes have been regarded as an ever-present problem. They kill thousands of sheep and cattle each year and a family of dingoes may sometimes kill a score or more livestock in one night.

Consequently, farmers have taken firm steps against the dogs. Thousands of square miles of sheep country have been fenced off, at a considerable cost. However, there is evidence that dingoes also play a significant role in maintaining an ecological balance in the region by suppressing populations of certain animals.

Thousands of dingoes have been shot or poisoned as the result of a hunting bounty placed on them. However, despite predictions in the early 20th century that they would soon become extinct, dingoes are still common, even in fairly well-populated areas. A greater problem than ordinary dingoes are the rogues, such as those that are wounded and therefore unable to hunt wild prey, or dingo-collie crosses, that make a speciality of killing sheep. Very large bounties may be offered for killing such a rogue.

The greatest threat to dingoes today is crossbreeding with domestic dogs. Until Europeans arrived on the continent, dingoes had remained free from contact with Asian or European dog breeds. However, after this time they began to interbreed with domestic dogs introduced by European settlers. Scientists believe that at present up to one-third of the dingoes in some areas of Australia are hybrids. If this situation persists, it is likely that in due course true dingoes will be wiped out as a species.

Dingoes generally hunt alone or in pairs. Occasionally, in areas where only large prey is available, they may hunt cooperatively.

DIPPER

Well-oiled waterbirds

Dippers flit about waterside rocks and boulders and walk and fly in and out of the water. Under their plumage is a thick layer of down that helps to insulate them and to repel water. Such is the effectiveness of their thick body feathers that dippers can withstand extremely low water temperatures in the winter. They can even feed under ice if necessary.

Dippers have large preen glands that supply all the oil needed to keep their plumage waterproof. The birds also have movable flaps over their nostrils and well-developed third eyelids, known as nictitating membranes, to keep out spray. Unlike other waterbirds however, dippers do not have webbed feet. Their feet are like those of most perching birds. As a result they have to paddle rapidly to make headway on the water's surface.

When a dipper is underwater, it uses its wings to swim through the water and its feet to walk along the bottom. Unlike other diving birds, such as cormorants, grebes and loons, dippers are very buoyant, although this does not seem to impair their ability to stay on the bottom of fast-flowing streams and rivers. At one time it was believed that the flow of water over a dipper's back pressed it against the bottom. It is currently accepted that the dipper prevents itself from rising though the water by powerful wingbeats.

Apart from running in and out of water, a dipper can also dive in and surface and take off without pausing. The usual duration of a dive is about 10 seconds in 1–2 feet (30–60 cm) of water. Dippers can stay underwater for up to half a minute and have been known to go down to a depth of 20 feet (6 m).

Chase prey underwater

Dippers are hard hit by severe winters, but where the ice is thin and there are plenty of holes, or where there is an air space between the water and the ice, they are able to continue feeding. The bulk of their food is insect larvae, including caddis flies, dragonflies and stoneflies. They also take water beetles, crustaceans, worms and mollusks, and catch small fish, such as minnows, and newts, searching either among boulders or along the streambed. Often a dipper

The white-throated dipper lives along fast-flowing streams in Europe and western Asia. Dippers are the only passerines, or perching birds, to lead a truly aquatic life.

THE DIPPERS, OF WHICH THERE ARE five very similar species, are wrenlike birds with short wings and tails. They grow to a length of up to 8 inches (20 cm), roughly the size of the starling, *Sturnus vulgaris*, or a small thrush. Dippers dwell along clear, fast-flowing rivers and streams, and lead a life quite unlike that of any other bird. They are the only truly aquatic members of the large order Passeriformes, or perching birds.

Dippers are nonmigratory birds, though they may descend to lower elevations or fly to the south of their range during severe winters. The white-throated dipper, *Cinclus cinclus*, with brown plumage and a white bib, is found over most of Europe and in some parts of western Asia. In Asia its range overlaps with that of the brown dipper, *C. pallasii*, but the latter species keeps to streams on the lower slopes of mountains. The American dipper, *C. mexicanus*, with a slate gray body and brown head, lives in the west of North and Central America from Alaska south to Panama. The white-capped dipper, *C. leucocephalus*, inhabits the Andes Mountains, while northwest Argentina and southwest Bolivia are home to the threatened rufous-throated dipper, *C. shulzi*.

AMERICAN DIPPER

CLASS	**Aves**
ORDER	**Passeriformes**
FAMILY	**Cinclidae**
GENUS AND SPECIES	***Cinclus mexicanus***

ALTERNATIVE NAME
American water ouzel (archaic)

WEIGHT
1¾–2½ oz. (50–72 g)

LENGTH
**Head to tail: about 7½ in. (19 cm);
wingspan: 12–13¾ in. (30–35 cm)**

DISTINCTIVE FEATURES
**Stocky, compact body; short wings and tail;
sooty gray plumage with brownish head**

DIET
**Mainly aquatic invertebrates, especially
insect larvae; some small fish**

BREEDING
**Age at first breeding: 1 year; breeding
season: March–June; number of eggs:
4 or 5; incubation period: 15–17 days;
fledging period: 24–25 days; breeding
interval: 1 year**

LIFE SPAN
Up to 8 years

HABITAT
**Fast-flowing mountain streams up to
tree line at 11,500 ft. (3,500 m); also on
slow-moving rivers with artificial rapids,
such as near water mills**

DISTRIBUTION
**Pacific coastline of North America from
Alaska south to California and east as far
as Rocky Mountains; northwestern Mexico
south to Panama**

STATUS
Locally common

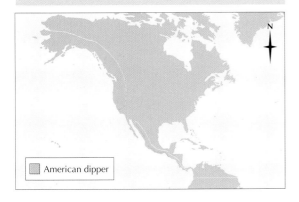

American dipper

will stand on a submerged boulder and catch small animals as they float past in the water. At fish farms dippers can become a pest by eating fish eggs and very young trout.

Bankside nests

A pair of dippers establishes and guards a territory that consists of a stretch of stream or river about ¼–½ mile (0.4–0.8 km) long. Neighboring pairs are usually well spread out with some distance between territories. Nests are made in banks and cliffs overlooking the water and in stone walls, under bridges and among tree roots. Only occasionally are they found at any distance from the water. The nests are cup-shaped and 8–12 inches (20–30 cm) in diameter. They are made chiefly of moss and intertwined grasses, lined with grasses and leaves and covered with a roof of moss. There are usually four or five eggs, brooded by the female alone. She leaves the nest only rarely, to feed. The eggs hatch in 15–17 days and the chicks stay in the nest for 3½–4 weeks, depending on the species.

Nests vulnerable to flooding

In 1962 James Alder, an ornithologist from the north of England, was studying dippers. After a period of heavy rain, the stream that he was observing became so swollen that Alder believed all dipper nests there would be destroyed. However, two of the nests were built in the bank under an overhanging flap of turf, which had been left behind as the bank underneath had been washed away. The parent dippers were able to continue feeding their chicks, diving into the water with billfulls of food and reappearing seconds later with bills empty. Later inspection of the nests showed that the water had lapped them, but that air had been trapped inside under the overhangs, saving the chicks.

Dippers can swim and walk underwater. They are capable of staying submerged for about 30 seconds, and of descending to depths of up to 20 feet (6 m).

DIVING BEETLE

Diving beetles are carnivorous and hunt worms, insect larvae, tadpoles and even small fish. They also feed on dead animals that have fallen into the water. Pictured above is the great diving beetle.

THERE ARE ABOUT 3,500 SPECIES of diving beetles in the world, in the family Dytiscidae. This total includes 41 North American genera, containing about 476 species. The European great diving beetle, *Dytiscus marginalis*, is sometimes known simply as dytiscus, after its genus. The great diving beetle is oval, 1¼ inches (3 cm) long and olive-black above with the thorax and wing coverts margined with yellow. Although it can fly, the beetle spends most of its time in water, swimming mainly with its broadened hind legs. These are fringed with bristles to offer greater resitance to the water and are used like oars. Most species are much smaller than the great diving beetle, but otherwise all have a similar appearance. *Dytiscus* diving beetles are very good fliers. If their pond or marsh dries up they are able to disperse and colonize new bodies of water.

Aqualung beetles

Diving beetles are most frequently found in still water containing plenty of waterweed. The beetles do not have gills and are not able to absorb oxygen directly from the water. They must take in air at the water's surface. To do this a beetle first raises its hind end foremost to push the tip of the abdomen just above the water. Then it raises its wing coverts slightly so that air is drawn into a pair of spiracles (breathing pores). Air is also drawn in under the wing coverts and trapped as bubbles among the fine bristles covering the back of the abdomen. The remaining spiracles draw on this store of air while the beetle is submerged.

Voracious feeders

Male and female diving beetles are easily distinguished. The wing cases of the female are marked with grooves running lengthwise. Those of the male are smooth, and there are circular pads on the front pair of legs. These have a sucker on the underside and are sticky. The male uses the pads to cling to the female when mating in spring. She lays her eggs one at a time, making a slit with her ovipositor in the stem of a water plant in which to deposit the eggs.

Diving beetles prey on almost any aquatic animal of suitable size. The larvae are one of the most formidable freshwater carnivores. When fully grown, the larvae are 2 inches (5 cm) long, with sharp calliper-like jaws. They may walk over the bottom or swim using their hair-fringed legs to propel themselves. Like adults, diving beetle larvae also come to the surface to breathe, taking in air through the tip of the tail. When they are ready to pupate, the larvae crawl out onto land and make mud cells in which they metamorphose into adults.

Each jaw of the larva is tubular. Once prey, such as a small fish or tadpole, has been seized, digestive juices are pumped down the jaws into the prey's body. This converts the tissues into a predigested soup, which is then sucked up through the jaws. The process continues until the body of the prey is an empty husk. By contrast, the adult diving beetle chews its food. Both larva and adult prey on live prey and carrion, even eating their own kind at times.

Water tigers

A diving beetle has a voracious appetite and attacks without hesitation. The very young larva doubtless falls victim to bottom-feeding fish but the fully grown larva and the adult beetle can readily defend themselves. Some idea of the force of their attack may be judged by the way their jaws can penetrate the bodies of other water beetles and disembowel a tadpole at the first lunge. In the United States, the larva has been nicknamed the water tiger due to the ferocity and power of its attack. The adult beetle may also give out a foul-smelling white fluid from its thorax when handled, and may possibly emit a yellow fluid reeking of ammonia from glands near the rear end of the body.

An adult diving beetle's smooth, streamlined body and oarlike hind legs are ideal for rapid movement underwater.

DIVING BEETLES

PHYLUM	**Arthropoda**
CLASS	**Insecta**
ORDER	**Coleoptera**
FAMILY	**Dytiscidae**
GENUS	***Dytiscus, Platambus, Acilius, Rhantus*; others; 41 genera in North America**
SPECIES	**3,500, including about 476 in North America**

ALTERNATIVE NAME
Larva: water tiger (U.S. only)

LENGTH
Adult: up to 1½ in. (4 cm)

DISTINCTIVE FEATURES
Adult: oval body; head drawn back into thorax; hind legs flattened and fringed with bristles; most species dark in color, striking yellow or red markings in some species. Larva: elongated body; very large jaws.

DIET
Wide range of other aquatic animals, including mosquito larvae, tadpoles, frogs and fish; also carrion and detritus

BREEDING
Varies according to species

LIFE SPAN
Up to 2 years

HABITAT
Still and stagnant fresh water, especially ponds and marshes

DISTRIBUTION
Worldwide; most species in warm regions

STATUS
Most species abundant; at least 23 species threatened

DIVING-PETREL

The common diving-petrel is silent at sea. At night on its nesting islands, however, it utters a wide range of far-carrying calls. These include cooing, mewing, chattering and wailing.

THE RAPID, WHIRRING FLIGHT of diving-petrels is unique within the petrel order, Procellariiformes. It contrasts with the slow, flapping and gliding flight of albatrosses, shearwaters and other petrels. Whereas most petrels have very long wings in relation to their body size, diving-petrels have compact bodies and relatively short wings.

The four species of diving-petrel are very similar in appearance, although they vary in size, measuring 6½–10 inches (16–25 cm) from head to tail. They are blackish above with white underparts. The strongly hooked bill is black and the legs are pale gray-blue. As in all petrels, the bill has long, tubular nostrils and the olfactory (associated with smell) part of the brain is highly developed. Petrels probably use their excellent sense of smell to locate feeding and breeding grounds, prey and other petrels.

Wander the southern oceans

Diving-petrels are ocean-going birds found in the cooler waters of the Southern Hemisphere. The most northern species is the Peruvian diving-petrel, *Pelecanoides garnotii*. Nearly twice as large as any other species of diving-petrel, it lives in the cool waters of the Humboldt Current that runs along the western coast of South

America. Also known as the *potoyunco*, the Peruvian diving-petrel occurs as far north as Peru. To the south the Magellanic diving-petrel, *P. magellani*, lives in the maze of channels and islands around Tierra del Fuego, southern Chile and southern Argentina.

The two other species of diving-petrel live on either side of the Antarctic Convergence, the distinct border separating warm and cool water that runs around the Antarctic continent. In the relatively warm waters to the north, the common diving-petrel, *P. urinatrix*, is found around the Falkland Islands, Tristan da Cunha and Gough Island, as well as around the islands south of Australia and New Zealand. It sometimes occurs off the coasts of New Zealand, where it is known as the jack diver. The South Georgia diving-petrel, *P. georgicus*, breeds on islands south of the Antarctic Convergence, such as the South Georgia Islands and South Sandwich Islands, and on islands to the north, such as Marion Island and Auckland Island. The common diving-petrel also breeds on South Georgia Island, but nests separately from the South Georgia diving-petrel. Some ornithologists now believe that certain island subspecies of the diving-petrels merit full species status. Further study of the relationships of the various breeding populations is required.

Feed at sea by night

Diving-petrels are nocturnal. They are attracted by the lights of ships, and often land on the decks. However, they have difficulty in taking off again because, like all petrels, they have to run over the ground or sea before becoming airborne. In the past, when the whaling factories around South Georgia and other subantarctic islands were lit up at night, large numbers of diving-petrels were attracted to them.

Most petrels search for food on the surface of the sea, flying low and then landing to pick up small prey from the upper few inches of the water. However, diving-petrels dive for their food, plunging into the water from a height of a few feet. Once in the water, they swim penguin-fashion, rowing with their wings rather than paddling with their feet. The actions of the wings are the same underwater as they are in the air. Diving-petrels have been seen plunging into one side of a wave and flying out of the other.

Diving-petrels live on plankton, crustaceans and small fish. Along the coast of South America, the Peruvian diving-petrel feeds on anchovies. At one time this species was an important

COMMON DIVING-PETREL

CLASS	**Aves**
ORDER	**Procellariiformes**
FAMILY	**Pelecanoididae**
GENUS AND SPECIES	***Pelecanoides urinatrix***

ALTERNATIVE NAMES
**Jack diver (New Zealand only);
kuaka (Stewart Island only);
flying penguin (Tristan da Cunha only)**

LENGTH
**Head to tail: about 8 in. (20 cm);
wingspan: about 16 in. (40 cm)**

DISTINCTIVE FEATURES
**Compact body; short wings; black, strongly
hooked bill with long, tubular nostrils; black
upperparts and white underparts; mottled
gray on sides of face, neck and throat**

DIET
**Mainly krill and copepods (crustaceans);
probably also small surface-feeding fish**

BREEDING
**Age at first breeding: not known; breeding
season: August–February in New Zealand
and southeast Australia, varies elsewhere;
number of eggs: 1; incubation period:
about 53 days; fledging period: 45–59 days;
breeding interval: 1 year**

LIFE SPAN
Not known

HABITAT
Open oceans; nests on oceanic islands

DISTRIBUTION
**Southern oceans between 34° S and 55° S;
main breeding grounds: Falkland Islands,
Tristan da Cunha, South Georgia, Gough
Island and subantarctic islands of New
Zealand and Australia**

STATUS
Common

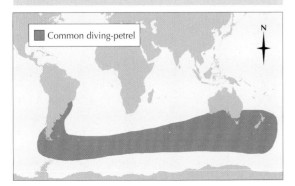

Common diving-petrel

producer of guano, a fertilizer composed mainly of seabird excrement. Peruvian diving-petrels bred in large numbers on the guano islands off Chile and Peru, nesting in burrows in the guano. Since the guano has been dug out and exported, the numbers of diving-petrels in these areas have greatly declined.

Night noises

The breeding season of diving-petrels depends on the latitude of their breeding grounds. The Peruvian diving-petrel lays throughout the year, whereas the South Georgia diving-petrel lays between November and February, in the middle of the short subantarctic summer. At the beginning of the breeding season, the diving-petrels can be heard courting at night. The slopes and cliffs behind the shores of islands in the southern oceans become very noisy with the courtship calls of the various species of petrels. Amid this continuous babble, the distinctive cooing, wailing, croaking or catlike mewing of the diving-petrels are clearly audible.

The female diving-petrel lays a single white egg at the end of a burrow dug in guano or in the soft, peaty soil under tussock grass. The burrow may be a few inches or a few feet long, depending on the soil type. Diving-petrels do not nest in clefts in rocks, which limits the extent of their breeding grounds. There is nothing else to prevent them from breeding farther south than the South Sandwich Islands, except that this is the southernmost range of tussock grass.

Chicks fed every night

The egg takes almost 8 weeks to hatch, an extremely long time considering the size of the bird. Both parents incubate, taking spells of one day each. This is unusual, as petrels usually incubate in spells of several days. It is similarly unusual for the chick to be fed every night. The parent flies straight to the nest hole and then crawls into it and caresses the chick's head with its bill. The chick then sets up an incessant call, whereupon the parent opens its bill. The chick thrusts its bill into the parent's mouth and the parent regurgitates food, semidigested crustaceans and fish, of a smooth consistency. When satisfied, the chick turns away and the parent settles down beside it. Later, when the chick has grown, the hole becomes too small for both birds, and the adult has to rest in a nearby hole. The chick finally leaves the nest hole when it is about 7–8 weeks old.

When nesting on islands, diving-petrels have no mammalian predators. However, they fall prey to introduced cats and rats and to a variety of large birds. Condors, caracaras and skuas all hunt diving-petrels.

DOGFISH

THE TERM DOGFISH APPLIES to several fish species. The species that was in Europe commonly dissected by students is the lesser spotted dogfish, once known as *Scyllium canicula*, now named *Scyliorhinus canicula*. Most North American biology students will have dissected the spiny dogfish, *Squalus acanthias*, or the Pacific dogfish, *S. suckleyi*. The last two species belong to the family Squalidae and, although small in size, are true sharks, whereas the lesser spotted dogfish is a cat shark, family Scyliorhinidae. The alligator dogfish or bramble shark, *Echinorhinus brucus*, feeds on spiny dogfish. In North America the term freshwater dogfish is also applied to the bowfin, *Amia calva*.

Very common in western European and Mediterranean waters, the lesser spotted dogfish, or rough hound, is slender, brownish with many small dark spots above and whitish below, and grows up to 3½ feet (1 m) long. The greater spotted dogfish or nurse hound, *Scyliorhinus stellaris*, is similar in appearance, except that its spots are larger and it may reach 5 feet (1.5 m) long. One of the largest cat sharks, it is found in the eastern Atlantic, from the Shetland Islands north of Scotland south to the Mediterranean. Both species are used for dissection purposes by medical and biology students. In most sharks there are two triangular dorsal fins, the first being the largest and set in the middle of the back. In dogfish these fins are equal in size and are sited close together and well back.

A dogfish has a comparatively long body and tail. Its pectoral and pelvic fins are moderate in size. The mouth is on the underside of the head, as are the nostrils, and there are five gill slits on each side behind the head; in bony fish these are hidden under a gill cover. The skin's rough texture is caused by the denticles (small teethlike projections) that grow out of it.

Chases prey by smell

The lesser spotted dogfish usually remains near sandy or gravel seabeds and at times gathers in enormous numbers. It frequently invades herring trawls and takes the bait of line fishermen, thus depriving the latter of a more profitable catch. Sometimes a trawl will come up with as many as 400 dogfish. While not of great commercial value, these are sold as food under the name of rock salmon in Britain.

To locate its prey, a dogfish works its way over the seabed, seeking food by smell. When it scents food, the dogfish stops, turns if necessary and picks it up. The eyes are not used in hunting. A dogfish hunting another fish will follow its trail, swimming along the same course, following every bend and turn and even passing its prey without seeing it should the latter double back.

Bottom-living fish form only a small proportion of a dogfish's overall intake of food. It mainly takes worms, sea cucumbers, prawns, shrimps and hermit crabs and some whelks, cuttlefish, squid and octopus.

Lesser spotted dogfish are bottom-dwellers. They feed primarily on marine invertebrates such as crustaceans. Dogfish locate their prey by scent rather than by sight.

DOGFISH

CLASS	**Chondrichthyes**
ORDER (1)	**Squaliformes**
FAMILY	**Spur dogfish, Squalidae**
GENUS AND SPECIES	**Spiny dogfish, *Squalus acanthias*; many others**

ORDER (2)	**Carcharhiniformes**
FAMILY	**Cat sharks, Scyliorhinidae**
GENUS AND SPECIES	**Lesser spotted dogfish, *Scyliorhinus canicula*; many others**

ALTERNATIVE NAMES
Adult: grayfish (North America only); rock salmon, rock eel, fluke (Britain only). Egg case: mermaid's purse (Britain only).

LENGTH
Up to 5¼ ft. (1.6 m)

DISTINCTIVE FEATURES
Elongated body; very rough skin, beset with denticles; mouth and nostrils on underside of head; 2 triangular dorsal fins of equal size, set well back on body; long tail

DIET
Mainly crustaceans, mollusks and other invertebrates; also fish, squid and octopus

BREEDING
Squalidae: bear live young; Scyliorhinidae: lay egg cases

LIFE SPAN
Up to 40 years or more, usually less

HABITAT
On or near to sandy and muddy seabeds

DISTRIBUTION
Subarctic south to subantarctic seas

STATUS
Mostly common; spiny dogfish numbers decreasing in eastern Atlantic

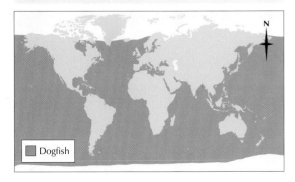

Dogfish

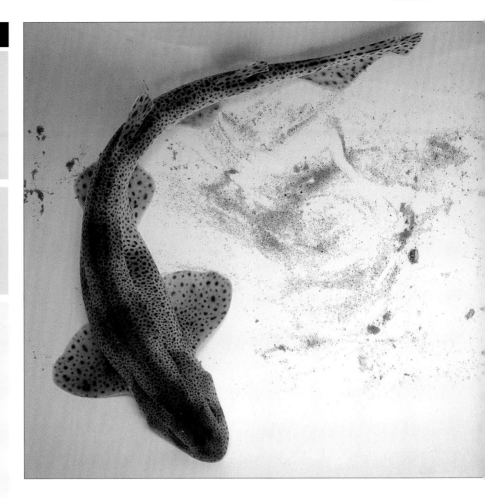

Born in a purse

The lesser spotted dogfish breeds in November–July, and during this time one-third of all the females will be carrying embryos. In mating, the male coils his body around the female, passing sperms into her oviducts with his claspers These are rigid parts of the pelvic fins, so named because it was once thought that the male dogfish used them to hold the female during mating. The eggs begin to develop in the oviduct and are later individually laid inside a brown, horny oblong case, sometimes called a mermaid's purse. The case is usually about 2 inches (5 cm) long. The eggs are laid throughout the year, but chiefly in spring and summer. At each corner of the egg case, or egg purse as it is also known, is a long tendril. As she lays pairs of eggs, the female moves around seaweed so that the tendrils wrap around them. Inside the capsule the baby dogfish is nourished from a large yolk sac, and 6 months after being laid it bursts out of the capsule, a miniature of its parents, but 3 inches (7.5 cm) long. Lesser spotted dogfish may live for up to 10 years.

The spiny spurdog

The spur, or spiny, dogfish has a stouter body than the lesser spotted variety and is slate-colored above, with small black-and-white spots

Dogfish are generally small in size and most inhabit shallow waters. All have long tails and dorsal fins positioned far along the back.

Dogfish have long been heavily exploited by humans. At various times they have been used to demonstrate anatomy in biology classes and to produce oil, fertilizer, sandpaper and food.

on the flanks and a whitish underside. There is a prominent spine at the front of each of the dorsal fins and the lines on these can be used to tell the age of the fish. The spines can cause a serious wound, exacerbated by the effect of the venom that is injected into the wound from tissue at the base of the spine. Spiny dogfish are found across the North Atlantic, ranging from Norway to the north coast of Africa and from western Greenland to Florida; their range also extends to the Mediterranean.

Spurdogs, or spiny spurdogs as they are also called, may live for over 40 years. They swim in large shoals in temperate seas, ranging from shallow waters to depths of 3,600 feet (1,100 m). Often the shoals consist of one sex only. In the summer they make long northward migrations of up to 1,200 miles (1,930 km) in large schools. Their diet is much the same as that of the lesser spotted dogfish, though they mainly feed on fish, taking other creatures only by chance.

Males mature sexually after 11 years; females first breed when they are 19–20 years old, coming inshore to mate. The males follow soon after from deeper water, and mating takes place during February and March, the babies being born 18–22 months later. Up to 20 live young are produced, each 8–12 inches (20–30 cm) long.

Relationship with humans

Dogfish were often used as a subject for dissection in biology classes: 100,000 were once used for this purpose every year in North America and Britain. In the past an oil was extracted from them in North America, and was used for

machinery, for dressing leather and in lamps. Fishmeal from dogfish was mixed with Peruvian guano to produce a fertilizer and their rough skin made shagreen, a sandpaper used in cabinetmaking. Today the flesh of dogfish is widely eaten, especially as fried fish, and is sold in Britain as rock eel, rock salmon and fluke. Dogfish is becoming increasingly popular as a food in Japan and also in North America, where it is known as grayfish.

Dogfish are still common in the world's oceans. Schools 1,000 strong have been known to follow herring shoals. Longline fishermen have taken 1,000 in a night and as many as 3,500 have been taken in one trawl. Twenty-seven million dogfish are caught per year off the coast of Massachusetts and Britain, Germany, France and Portugal landed 10,000 tons in 1964. Around the coasts of the United States spiny dogfish are abundant; indeed, fishers regard this species as a threat to the numbers of more profitable species in the region, such as cod, herring and haddock, all of which the spiny dogfish feed on. However, the size of the catches around European shores is gradually declining. Species such as the spiny dogfish are particularly vulnerable to the effects of overfishing, as both males and females reach sexual maturity late in life, litter size is small and the young develop for a considerable time within the mother before birth. On the eastern side of the Atlantic, concerns are growing that the main grounds supplying dogfish are being overfished. If the decline is not arrested, the principal losers will be the fish and chip shops in the south of England and northern Europe.

DOGS

DOG IS THE COMMON NAME for a member of the family Canidae, which includes the foxes, jackals, coyotes and wolves and their relatives. The dogs, or canids, are medium-sized carnivores of wide distribution, being found everywhere except Antarctica. They are adapted for hunting prey over relatively long distances, using superior endurance to wear down their quarry.

In general the dogs are more omnivorous (eating all types of food) than other members of the order Carnivora, such as the cats. Dogs are opportunists, with fruits, leaves, insects and carrion often forming part of their diet. However, the proportion of such alternative foodstuffs taken varies from species to species. Nearly half of the golden jackal's (*Canis aureus*) diet is plant-derived, whereas that of the culpeo fox (*Lycalopex culpaeus*) may be up to 97 percent meat. Dogs vary in social structure. Some species, such as the gray wolf, *Canis lupus*, and Cape hunting dog, *Lycaon pictus*, hunt in packs. A few species, including the sand or pale fox, *Vulpes pallida*, live in small family groups, while others, such as the red fox, *Vulpes vulpes*, are essentially solitary and territorial.

Evolution

The ancestors of the family Canidae date back 40 million years to the late Eocene period. The center of canid evolution was in North America, where the first dogs remained for

Dogs have large canine teeth and acute senses of smell and hearing. Most species, including the South American gray fox, Lycalopex griseus, have varied diets and are highly adaptable.

34 million years. The canids did not begin to diversify until the Miocene period, about 10 to 6 million years ago. At this time a split developed between the predecessors of modern wolves, coyotes and jackals on the one hand, and the ancestors of modern foxes on the other. Three new genera also appeared at this point: *Urocyon* (the North American gray foxes), *Nyctereutes* (the raccoon dog) and *Otocyon* (the bat-eared fox). These developments make it hard to establish precise relationships among the canids.

By the end of the Miocene era, 42 genera of canids had evolved. The canids also began to diversify geographically, spreading to Eurasia and Africa. Today, the bears are their closest relatives within the order Carnivora.

CLASSIFICATION
CLASS
Mammalia
ORDER
Carnivora
FAMILY
Canidae
NUMBER OF SPECIES
35

Dogs Family Tree

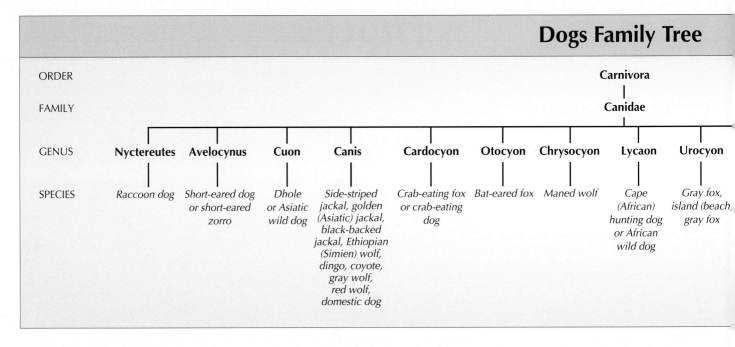

ORDER							Carnivora		
FAMILY							Canidae		
GENUS	Nyctereutes	Avelocynus	Cuon	Canis	Cardocyon	Otocyon	Chrysocyon	Lycaon	Urocyon
SPECIES	Raccoon dog	Short-eared dog or short-eared zorro	Dhole or Asiatic wild dog	Side-striped jackal, golden (Asiatic) jackal, black-backed jackal, Ethiopian (Simien) wolf, dingo, coyote, gray wolf, red wolf, domestic dog	Crab-eating fox or crab-eating dog	Bat-eared fox	Maned wolf	Cape (African) hunting dog or African wild dog	Gray fox, island (beach gray fox

The doglike branch of the Canidae includes the genera *Canis* (the domestic dogs, wolves, dingoes, coyotes and jackals), *Chrysocyon* (the maned wolf) and *Cerdocyon* (the crab-eating fox). In the foxlike branch of the family, evolutionary divergence has been partly along geographic lines. Separate genera are present in the Arctic (*Alopex*: the Arctic fox) and in South America (*Lycalopex*: the South American foxes or zorros), while the largest genus, *Vulpes*, is represented throughout North America, Africa and Eurasia.

Physical adaptations

The dogs weigh 9–150 pounds (4–70 kg) according to species but despite this considerable variation in size share a common hunting technique. This involves pursuit at moderately high speed until the prey tires, followed by a firm bite to the back of the neck. The large canine teeth lock together, and the prey is brought down.

Dogs have a digitigrade posture; that is, they walk on the front four, extended, toes rather than on the flat foot. This enhances leg length and hence speed, although the adaptation is less pronounced than in carnivores that rely on short bursts of very high speed, such as the cats. Dogs cannot retract their claws, unlike cats. As a result their claws suffer constant wear and are not sharp enough for killing prey and climbing.

The dogs are equipped with acute smell and hearing to enable them to detect and track prey. This is reflected in the long, strong muzzles and large pinnae, or ear flaps, that unify the appearance of the family. Dogs typically have a full set of teeth: 22 in the lower jaw and 20 in the upper jaw. This arrangement enables them to disembowel prey by biting the underbelly. Dogs can feed very quickly. For example, the dhole, *Cuon alpinus*, may devour up to 9 pounds (4 kg) of meat in an hour.

Sight and touch are less important to dogs than to carnivores that subdue prey by attacking the jugular vein on the underside of the neck. Examples of carnivores that use the latter technique are the cats, weasels and ermines.

Breeding

The timing of the reproductive cycle in dogs is related mainly to day length and to season. However, it is also determined by the availability

The Bengal or Indian fox, Vulpes bengalensis, *is one of several pale-colored dogs found mainly in open, semiarid country such as plains, steppe and mountain foothills.*

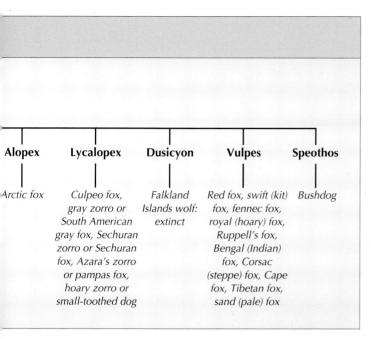

Alopex	Lycalopex	Dusicyon	Vulpes	Speothos
Arctic fox	Culpeo fox, gray zorro or South American gray fox, Sechuran zorro or Sechuran fox, Azara's zorro or pampas fox, hoary zorro or small-toothed dog	Falkland Islands wolf: extinct	Red fox, swift (kit) fox, fennec fox, royal (hoary) fox, Ruppell's fox, Bengal (Indian) fox, Corsac (steppe) fox, Cape fox, Tibetan fox, sand (pale) fox	Bushdog

Gestation is usually 60–63 days in the larger species of dogs and 50–57 days in the smaller species. The number of young, known as pups, varies from one to as many as 25 according to the abundance of food and to the mother's fitness and age. However, the average litter size—four to six pups—is remarkably consistent between species regardless of body weight.

Dogs usually protect their young from predators by hiding them in a den or burrow. The pups are normally blind at birth. Weaning from milk to regurgitated meat occurs at 2–8 weeks, depending on species. Parental care usually comes to an end during the fall, with the offspring reaching sexual maturity in time for the next mating season in spring.

Social organization

It is in the systems of social grouping that the life histories of the canids display the greatest diversity. Several species are monogamous, and some of these, among them the Arctic fox and golden jackal, pair for life. This type of social organization is associated with a strongly territorial, solitary lifestyle. Other species of dogs maintain packs and establish mating dominance hierarchies. The culpeo fox has a female hierarchy in which the position of the alpha (dominant) female is inherited by her most dominant female offspring. The gray wolf forms packs of three to 13 animals, which roam large territories. Only the alpha male and female (dominant pair) of each

of prey. Species found near the equator have a relatively long breeding season because climatic variation is limited in equatorial regions. The dhole, for instance, breeds from November to March. The golden jackal, *Canis aureus*, breeds during January and February in Africa but in the cooler climes of southeastern Europe delays breeding until April–May. The Arctic fox, *Alopex lagopus*, which breeds further north than any other dog, is also the last to breed, in April–July.

The kit fox, Vulpes velox macrotis, a small, large-eared dog of deserts in the southwestern United States, hunts by night to avoid the daytime heat. It preys on rabbits, rodents and insects.

Swift foxes, **Vulpes velox,** *form breeding pairs by late winter and the females give birth in February–April. Both parents hunt on behalf of the offspring, and the family disperses in the fall.*

pack breed. Species that form packs do so by retaining off-spring beyond the age of maturity. Wolf packs consist of both sexes, the subordinate members staying for 1–2 years before some of them leave to set up new packs of their own.

Related behavior is seen in the golden jackal and black-backed jackal, *Canis mesomelas.* In these species the offspring from previous litters, which are now young, sexually mature adults, sometimes return to their parents to help them rear a new litter. By doing so the helpers increase their parents' breeding success. This leads to greater overall transmission of the family's gene line than if they had immediately dispersed upon reaching maturity. In species that maintain matriarchal (female-dominated) packs the young males disperse and the young females stay to establish their rank.

As with all mammals, the degree of sociality in dogs is determined by prey density. If the prey species are large or live in large herds, the formation of packs is favored, as cooperative hunting overcomes the difficulties of catching such prey. If the prey species are relatively small or evenly distributed, territories and solitary hunting are favored.

Relationship with humans

The hunting ability of dogs, particularly the gray wolf, has led to fear and superstition in human culture. Many species have been heavily persecuted as a result. However, the spread of large-scale agriculture has produced a more equivocal relationship. Dogs control populations of rodents and lagomorphs (rabbits and hares), which can become pests of arable farming. Dogs have also been widely domesticated for use in hunting, to shepherd flocks of sheep and cattle, and as guard dogs and pets. The "negative" side of the partnership is the threat, usually more perceived than real, that wild dogs pose to livestock.

Persecution by humans and the loss of natural habitats have had a serious impact on many species of dogs. For example, the expansion of agriculture has led to the disappearance from the wild of the red wolf, *Canis rufus,* which is native to the southeast and south-central United States. It is classed as critically endangered by the I.U.C.N. (World Conservation Union) and only 300 captive animals now remain. Traps laid for gray wolves have decimated numbers of that species in much of the United States and have driven to extinction the Canadian populations of the northern swift fox, *Vulpes velox hebes.* The Ethiopian wolf, *Canis simensis,* is considered to be critically endangered, with fewer than 600 animals surviving in its stronghold, and the Cape hunting dog is endangered. Several other species are vulnerable.

For particular species see:
- ARCTIC FOX • BAT-EARED FOX • BUSHDOG
- CAPE HUNTING DOG • COYOTE • CRAB-EATING FOX
- DHOLE • DINGO • FENNEC FOX • GRAY FOX
- GRAY WOLF • JACKAL • MANED WOLF
- RACCOON DOG • RED FOX • SHORT-EARED DOG

DOLPHINFISH

T HE TERM DOLPHINFISH is used as the common name of the only two species of fish in the family Coryphaenidae. The name sometimes leads to confusion between these animals and the true dolphins. The mammals and fish were probably both given the name dolphin because of their similar shape and habit of leaping from the water's surface.

The best known of the two dolphinfish is the common dolphinfish, *Coryphaena hippurus*, which grows up to 6½ feet (2 m) long and reaches a maximum weight of nearly 90 pounds (40 kg). The male has a squarish head, while that of the female is more rounded; both are heavier in the front half of the body, which tapers away to end in a forked tail. The dorsal fin runs almost the length of the back. Live common dolphinfish have striking metallic blue-green upperparts, with silvery underparts. Dying specimens, or those hauled from the water, undergo spectacular changes in their colors. Floating logs, kelp and flotsam often attract this species. In parts of the Pacific, the common dolphinfish is known as *Ma-hi Ma-hi*, and it is referred to as the *dorado* in Portuguese and Spanish-speaking regions.

The second species, the pompano dolphinfish, *C. equiselis*, has a maximum length of 2½ feet (75 cm) and is seldom more than 1 foot (30 cm) long. It is brightly colored, with silvery tints and distinct dark spots on its sides. The pompano dolphinfish ranges across the tropical Atlantic,

including the Caribbean and the Gulf of Mexico. Adult pompano dolphinfish are mostly limited to the surface areas of tropical seas and are rarely caught. The young are more easily seen, as they are attracted by lights at night.

The two species are very similar in appearance and are difficult to tell apart when young and of similar size. It is possible to tell juveniles apart by comparing body and mouthparts. *C. equiselis* has a deeper body than *C. hippurus*, and its teeth cover most of its tongue. It is also possible to distinguish the species by counting the rays in the dorsal fin; *C. hippurus* has more rays in the fin than *C. equiselis*. In the Atlantic, *C. hippurus* has 58 to 66 rays while *C. equiselis* has 52 to 59. In the Pacific, *C. hippurus* has 55 to 65 dorsal fin rays; *C. equiselis* has 48 to 56.

Hunts the flying fish

Dolphinfish live in tropical seas, singly or in schools. They swim fast, reaching speeds of up to 40 miles per hour (64 km/h). Such speeds are necessary to catch flying fish, which are an important item in their diet. Dolphinfish eject themselves out of the water in pursuit of their gliding prey. At other times they will swim underneath as the flying fish is airborne, ready to snap it up as it reenters the sea. Flying fish, however, are not the only prey. More than 30 species of fish belonging to 19 families have been identified in the stomach contents of dolphinfish.

Dolphinfish have striking turquoise blue or green upperparts and silvery underparts. These colors rapidly change when the fish are removed from the sea.

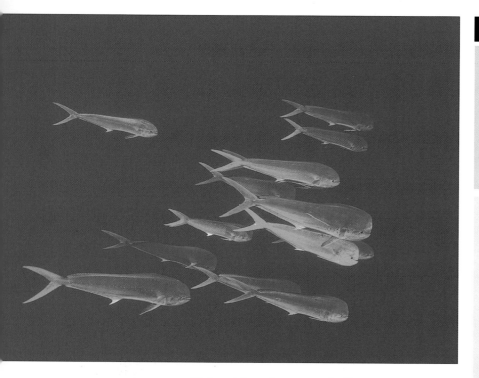

Common dolphinfish often swim in small schools. They feed on several surface-living fish and often hunt near patches of kelp or flotsam on the surface of the sea.

Fish with a fast metabolism

Most probably dolphinfish fall prey to larger predatory fish, particularly when young. However, little is known of the early stages of their life history except that growth is very rapid. Dolphinfish kept in the Marine Studios in Florida had to be fed three times a day, suggesting that the species have a high metabolic rate that causes them rapidly to use up energy and require a large quantity of food to replace it. Part of this energy consumption is taken up in rapid growth. The 52 captive dolphinfish in the Marine Studios were at most 18 inches (46 cm) long and weighed 1½ pounds (0.7 kg) when first put into the aquarium. One was measured and weighed 4½ months later; it was 45 inches (115 cm) long and weighed 25 pounds (11.5 kg). Three months later two more were measured and found to be 50 inches (130 cm) in length up to 37 pounds (17 kg) in weight. Scientists believe that the life span of a dolphinfish may be as short as 3 years.

Studies have been made on many fish to find the ratio between the surface area of the gills, a measure of how much oxygen the fish can take in, and the weight of the body. Scientists have discovered that the highest ratio was that of the menhaden, with the figure of 2¾ square inches (17.75 sq cm) of gill per gram of body weight. The second highest ratio belonged to the mackerel with 1¾ square inches (11.3 sq cm) per gram of body weight. Third was the mullet with 1½ square inches (9.7 sq cm) and fourth was the dolphinfish with 1 square inch (6.5 sq cm) per gram of body weight. All four are fast-growing fish, and the results of the test would suggest that all are relatively short-lived.

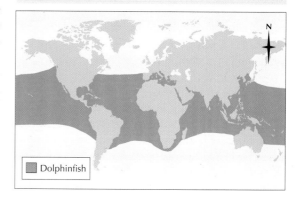

Dolphinfish

DOLPHINS AND PORPOISES

DOLPHINS AND PORPOISES OCCUR IN many of the world's marine habitats, ranging from the Arctic to the Antarctic and from deep seas to coastal waters. Each species of dolphin or porpoise is perfectly adapted to fit a specific environmental niche. All dolphins, porpoises and whales originated from a land-dwelling ancestor that lived over 50 million years ago. The skeletons of modern dolphins and porpoises still display the remnants of pelvic and hip bones that once held their ancestor's hind limbs.

Classification

Whales, dolphins and porpoises belong to the order Cetacea. Members of this order are generally hairless and have a torpedo-shaped body, paddle-shaped forelimbs, no hind limbs, a blowhole at the top of the head and a flattened tail. This order is split into two suborders: the Mysticeti, or baleen whales, and the Odontoceti, or toothed whales.

The suborder Mysticeti contains large whales that feed by sieving huge amounts of plankton from the sea. Its members include the humpback whale (*Megaptera novaeangliae*), gray whale (*Eschrichtius robustus*) and blue whale (*Balaenoptera musculus*). These species are discussed in a separate guidepost article. The suborder Odontoceti comprises nine families of toothed cetaceans. Four of these families are not commonly thought of as dolphins or porpoises: they are the beaked whales (Ziphiidae), white whales (Monodontidae), sperm whales (Physeteridae) and pygmy and dwarf sperm whales (Kogiidae). For this reason these species are also discussed elsewhere. This article concerns the five remaining families in the suborder Odontoceti, which contain all of the species popularly known as dolphins and porpoises.

By leaping into the air as they travel, dolphins are able to increase their speed to more than 30 miles per hour (48 km/h).

It is possible to distinguish a dolphin from a porpoise by comparing their teeth. While a dolphin's teeth are conical, those of a porpoise are flattened and spade-shaped. Porpoises are also smaller than most dolphin species, generally reaching no more than 5 feet (1.5 m) in length, and never have beaks. Most porpoises have a small triangular dorsal fin and are a combination of black, white and gray in color. They are usually found around coastlines, though Dall's porpoise, *Phocoenoides dalli*, the largest species, is sometimes found in deeper waters in the North Pacific. Porpoises feed on prawns, squid and fish.

The name porpoise is sometimes used in North America as a general term to describe any small cetacean. However, it is only the six species in the family Phocoenidae that may be accurately described as porpoises.

The family referred to as true dolphins (Delphinidae) consists of 32 species, including the dolphins, orca or killer whale (*Orcinus orca*) and pilot whales. The smaller

Dolphins and Porpoises Family Tree

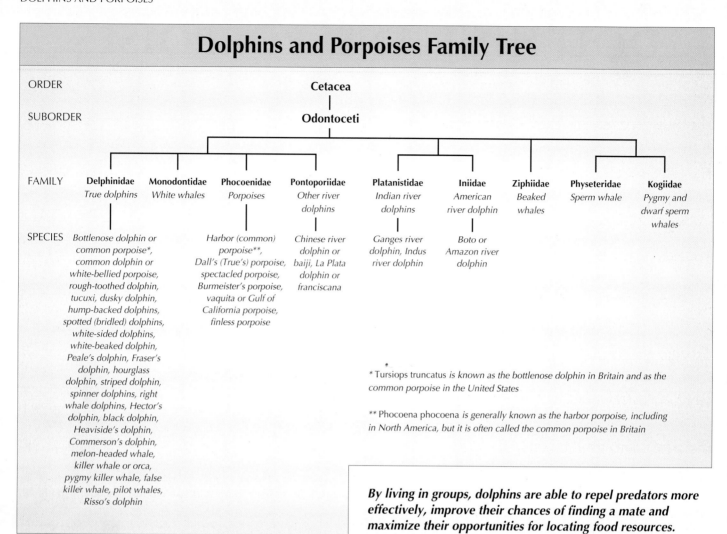

ORDER Cetacea

SUBORDER Odontoceti

FAMILY

Delphinidae	Monodontidae	Phocoenidae	Pontoporiidae	Platanistidae	Iniidae	Ziphiidae	Physeteridae	Kogiidae
True dolphins	*White whales*	*Porpoises*	*Other river dolphins*	*Indian river dolphins*	*American river dolphin*	*Beaked whales*	*Sperm whale*	*Pygmy and dwarf sperm whales*

SPECIES

Bottlenose dolphin or common porpoise*, common dolphin or white-bellied porpoise, rough-toothed dolphin, tucuxi, dusky dolphin, hump-backed dolphins, spotted (bridled) dolphins, white-sided dolphins, white-beaked dolphin, Peale's dolphin, Fraser's dolphin, hourglass dolphin, striped dolphin, spinner dolphins, right whale dolphins, Hector's dolphin, black dolphin, Heaviside's dolphin, Commerson's dolphin, melon-headed whale, killer whale or orca, pygmy killer whale, false killer whale, pilot whales, Risso's dolphin

Harbor (common) porpoise**, Dall's (True's) porpoise, spectacled porpoise, Burmeister's porpoise, vaquita or Gulf of California porpoise, finless porpoise

Chinese river dolphin or baiji, La Plata dolphin or franciscana

Ganges river dolphin, Indus river dolphin

Boto or Amazon river dolphin

* Tursiops truncatus *is known as the bottlenose dolphin in Britain and as the common porpoise in the United States*

** Phocoena phocoena *is generally known as the harbor porpoise, including in North America, but it is often called the common porpoise in Britain*

By living in groups, dolphins are able to repel predators more effectively, improve their chances of finding a mate and maximize their opportunities for locating food resources.

Delphinidae are called dolphins on the basis of size. There is no evolutionary trait separating them from pilot whales, genus *Globicephala*, and killer whales. Dolphins grow 4–13 feet (1.2–4 m) long. Most are streamlined with a backward-curving dorsal fin, one blowhole, a clearly defined beak and sharp teeth. Dolphins with well-developed beaks are generally fish eaters, while those with a less developed beak and fewer teeth feed mostly on squid.

As well as the true dolphins and the porpoises (Phocoenidae) there are three families of river dolphins (Platanistidae, Iniidae and Pontoporiidae). They contain five species, which live in rivers, coastal habitats and estuaries in Asia and South America. These are: the Indus river dolphin (*Platanista minor*), Ganges river dolphin (*Platanista gangetica*), La Plata dolphin (*Pontoporia blainvillei*), boto or Amazon river dolphin (*Inia geoffrensis*) and baiji or Chinese river dolphin (*Lipotes vexillifer*). The river dolphins are characterized by their long, slim jaws with which they feed on fish and shrimps. The La Plata dolphin, which inhabits the salt waters around coastlines, also feeds on squid and octopuses.

Echolocation

Dolphins and porpoises employ a sonar or echolocation system to navigate and to locate their prey. They emit a series of clicks by vibrating the air in their nasal sacs. The sacs are situated behind the melon, a lump of fatty tissue filled with oil that lies in front of the skull. Scientists believe that the melon focuses the clicks into a series of sounds varying between 20 and 800 vibrations per second. When these sounds hit an object they are reflected back to the mammal, which is able to calculate how far away the object is by the time it takes the

The dark and light spots on the skin of the spotted dolphin are absent at birth but increase in number and enlarge with age. The spotting is more intense in certain geographical regions, such as the Pacific coasts of Mexico and Central America.

echo to bounce back. It is possible that these ultrasonic frequencies can kill small prey such as anchovies, or confuse a school of fish so that they are easier to catch.

Reproduction

Dolphin and porpoise breeding peaks from spring to fall. During this period temperate and Arctic regions have longer days and higher temperatures, which promote greater concentrations of plankton and, in turn, larger populations of the fish and squid that dolphins eat. There is intense competition between males for mates. They chase each other, smack their jaws loudly and bite aggressively to discourage rivals. The female accepts a male by rolling onto her back on the surface, whereupon the male lies on top of her and the two mate.

The gestation period is 10–12 months, after which one calf is born. As it has no air in its lungs when it is born, the calf lacks buoyancy and has to be carried to the surface by the mother for its first breath. This is a dangerous time, as the smell of the blood shed at birth can attract sharks. The mother suckles her young for up to 18 months, although it can eat fish after 4 months. A female dolphin or porpoise gives birth every 2 or 3 years, producing up to eight offspring during her lifetime. The male parent has little contact with the offspring after birth. Pair bonding is evidently not required after reproduction, as both male and female dolphins and porpoises have several partners.

Dolphin and porpoise acrobatics

Dolphins and porpoises often ride the waves created by the bows of boats. Because it is easier to travel faster in air than in water several species, such as the pantropical spotted dolphin, *Stenella attenuata*, and Atlantic spotted dolphin, *S. frontalis*, regularly leap clear of the water. Spinner dolphins, *S. longirostris*, not only leap up to 10 feet (3.5 m) into the air, but also spin around on their longitudinal axis up to seven times in a single leap. Such aerial activity may act as a means of communication, especially when accompanied by loud re-entry in which the dolphin lands on its side, front or back. The habit may also be a means of dislodging ectoparasites. The striped dolphin, *S. coeruleoalba*, can leap vertically from the water (a movement known as breaching) to heights of 23 feet (7 m). Along with with several other oceanic dolphins such as the dusky dolphin, *Lagenorhynchus obscurus*, the striped dolphin is capable of striking acrobatics including arch-shaped leaps, tailspins and somersaults. In some species, such as Hector's dolphin, *Cephalorhynchus hectori*, a pair of dolphins may leap together as part of a courtship ritual.

Dall's porpoise may be the fastest small cetacean, reaching speeds of 34 miles per hour (55 km/h). It rarely leaps from the water, but it zigzags and darts around boats at great speed.

Conservation

Dolphin populations have been falling dramatically for many years, particularly in the eastern tropical Pacific, the northeast Atlantic and the waters around Japan, Peru, Venezuela and Chile. Dolphin meat is a delicacy in Japan, and an estimated 14,500 dolphins are killed every year for consumption.

Some dolphin species, such as the pantropical spotted dolphin and spinner dolphin, form large groups numbering several thousand. Yellowfin tuna often follow below them, possibly hoping to take advantage of the dolphins' superior food-finding talent. This association has been used to great advantage by the tuna fishing industry. Large groups of dolphins are spotted, often using helicopters. Speedboats then race to the site to chase and scare the dolphins. Once the school stops, the large purse seiner boats steam up to set their nets, catching and killing both tuna and dolphins. It is estimated that at least 6 million dolphins have died in the eastern tropical Pacific in this way over the past 30 years. However, it is possible to catch tuna without harming dolphins, and in the early 1990s growing consumer pressure forced some tuna companies to sell only fish that had not been caught in this way. Tuna fishing has decreased in the eastern tropical Pacific and many fishers are now using purse seine nets to catch only free-swimming tuna schools or are switching to pole and line fishing.

Rising pollution levels caused by the release of toxic chemicals into seas and rivers are also adversely affecting dolphin numbers. Chemicals such as PCBs (polychlorinated biphenyls) build up in dolphins' bodies and are stored in their blubber and fat reserves. When the dolphins use these reserves, the toxins are released into their bloodstream, affecting their ability to reproduce and their immunity to disease. In 1987 UK-based industries dumped more than 11 million tons (10 million tonnes) of waste directly into the sea, including sewage and highly polluting industrial waste. This practice has now been stopped, but considerable damage has already been done to regional marine life, especially in the North Sea.

All five species of river-dwelling dolphins are threatened by increasing levels of sewage and industrial pollution. Many rivers are also becoming choked with silt that washes down from deforested hillsides. The construction of dams and other water-controlling devices disrupts the habitats of river systems, often with adverse consequences for these species.

The I.U.C.N. (World Conservation Union) currently classifies eight species of dolphins and porpoises as critically endangered, endandered or vulnerable. A further 25 species are potentially at risk but cannot be classified at present due to the lack of accurate population data.

For particular species see:
- BEAKED WHALE • BELUGA WHALE
- BOTTLENOSE DOLPHIN • COMMON DOLPHIN
- FALSE KILLER WHALE • KILLER WHALE • NARWHAL
- PILOT WHALE • PORPOISE • RIVER DOLPHIN

Dolphins (dusky dolphin, above) may breach for different reasons. For instance, the impact at landing may frighten fish, concentrating them into tighter shoals that are easier to catch.

DORMOUSE

ORMICE ARE LARGE-EYED, long-tailed rodents that resemble squirrels and rats more closely than they do mice. The species known in Britain as the common dormouse, *Muscardinus avellanarius*, is not the most common species in the rest of Europe. It is less confusing to call it the hazel dormouse, a name derived from the German *haselmaus*, after the animal's appetite for hazelnuts.

Appearance of the dormice

The tail of the hazel dormouse is 2¼–3 inches (5.5–7.5 cm) long and rather thick and bushy, though it is not as bushy as that of typical squirrels. The head and body measure 2⅓–3½ inches (6–9 cm). The fur is yellowish brown; the throat, chest and toes are white. The hazel dormouse is one of the smallest species of dormice. Other small species include the desert dormouse, *Selevinia betpakdalaensis*, certain African dormice of the genus *Graphiurus* and the forest dormice of the genus *Dryomys*.

The edible, or fat, dormouse, *Glis glis*, is the largest dormouse, about 12 inches (30 cm) long from nose to tail. It is also the most squirrel-like in appearance due to its bushy tail. The eyes appear to be very large because of a ring of black fur around them. The coat is short, thick and silvery gray, with creamy white underparts. The garden dormouse, *Eliomys quercinus*, has a black tufted tail and a black patch behind each eye. The Japanese dormouse, *Glirulus japonicus*, has a short tail and a black stripe down the back and resembles the hazel dormouse. Forest dormice have black face masks, while African dormice have black-and-white patches on the face. The mouse-tailed dormice of the genus *Myomimus* were originally known only from skull fragments found in owl pellets (regugitated pellets containing indigestible prey remains such as bones and fur). The first live specimen was found in 1959 in southern Bulgaria.

A widespread family

Dormice are a widespread group of rodents, represented in much of Europe and Asia. The range of the garden dormouse extends south into North Africa. The African dormice are found south of the Sahara Desert.

The hazel dormouse lives in many parts of Europe and southwestern Asia, from Sweden southward to Sicily. At one time common in

Dormice are small, climbing rodents intermediate in form between rats and squirrels. The garden dormouse lives in vineyards, gardens and orchards.

HAZEL DORMOUSE

CLASS	**Mammalia**
ORDER	**Rodentia**
FAMILY	**Gliridae (also known as Myoxidae or Muscardinidae)**
GENUS AND SPECIES	***Muscardinus avellanarius***

ALTERNATIVE NAMES
Common dormouse; sleeper (archaic)

WEIGHT
½–1½ oz. (15–40 g)

LENGTH
Head and body: 2⅓–3½ in. (6–9 cm); tail: 2¼–3 in. (5.5–7.5 cm)

DISTINCTIVE FEATURES
Large eyes; pointed muzzle; thick, bushy tail; yellowish brown coat, with white throat, chest and toes

DIET
Mainly nuts (especially hazelnuts), seeds, fruits, shoots, buds, bark and insects; probably also bird eggs and nestlings

BREEDING
Age at first breeding: less than 1 year; breeding season: summer, with peaks in June–early July and late July–early August; number of young: usually 3 to 5; gestation period: 22–24 days; breeding interval: 1 or 2 litters per year

LIFE SPAN
Up to 4 years

HABITAT
Deciduous woodland with plenty of undergrowth and shrubs

DISTRIBUTION
Southern England east to Ural Mountains and south to Mediterranean

STATUS
Declining in much of range; rare in Britain

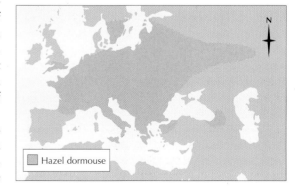

Hazel dormouse

In late summer the hazel dormouse gorges itself on berries and nuts to lay down fat reserves. These will sustain it during its profound winter sleep. Dormice lose up to half their body weight when hibernating.

southern England, it used to be as popular a pet as the white mice and hamsters now kept by schoolchildren. The North American gray squirrel, *Sciurus carolinensis*, which was introduced to Britain and soon became firmly established there, forced the hazel dormouse out of its native habitat.

The edible dormouse also lives in Europe and southwestern Asia. Its range extends from the Baltic Sea south to the Pyrenees, eastward to the Caspian Sea and south into Israel. In 1902 the species was introduced into England when Lord Rothschild released animals at Tring Park. There is now a flourishing edible dormouse population to the northwest of London, which is confined within a triangle bounded by the towns of Aylesbury, Beaconsfield and Luton.

Nocturnal woodland residents

The hazel dormouse lives in deciduous woodland, especially where such plants as honeysuckles and brambles form a thick layer of undergrowth. Shredded honeysuckle bark is a reliable indication of the presence of dormice. The hazel dormouse is very agile, spending most of its time in trees, and is skilled at climbing slim twigs. During the day it sleeps in nests of honeysuckle bark, leaves and grasses.

The edible dormouse spends much of its time in trees, especially in oak woodland or in woodland containing a combination of holm oak, ash and pine trees. Such habitats offer the dormouse abundant supplies of fruit as well as plentiful hollows in old tree trunks where it may shelter. The edible dormouse prefers woodland without undergrowth, in contrast to the hazel, garden and forest dormice, all of which favor a shrub layer. The garden dormouse spends more time on the ground than other dormice and is often found among rocks.

All dormice are nocturnal and spend the day in nests in trees or in the ground. In the summer the edible dormouse sometimes adapts an abandoned bird nest, rabbit run or squirrel's treetop nest for its own needs. The nest is spherical and is usually constructed out of leafy branches and twigs. The edible dormouse is also sometimes found in outhouses and attics.

Dormant dormice

Unlike most animals, which remain alert for signs of danger even when apparently asleep, dormice sleep very profoundly. During hibernation a dormouse abandons all holes apart from those that have south-facing entrances or are sufficiently protected from the weather. Most dormice hibernate in underground holes, where several may huddle together.

When preparing to hibernate, a dormouse rolls itself up, chin resting on the belly, feet folded around the muzzle and tail wrapped over the head. The entire body gradually becomes rigid. Common and edible dormice, which are the only British rodents to hibernate, go to sleep in late October and wake up in April. Before retiring, they put on weight, eating the large quantities of food that other rodents store in caches for the winter. The daily sleeps last longer and longer until the dormice no longer wake up during the night. Their body temperature drops until it is just above that of the surrounding air and their heartbeat and breathing almost stop.

The start of hibernation seems to be triggered by overeating during the fall rather than by the arrival of cold weather. Occasionally, a dormouse will wake up during the winter and leave its nest to go foraging. Dormice sometimes lose half their body weight during hibernation. Their sleeping state leaves them highly vulnerable to predators; it has been estimated that in the British Isles four out of every five dormice are killed during hibernation. Magpies, foxes, badgers, weasels, ermines and rats all seek out sleeping dormice in their nests.

Hazel dormice feed on hazelnuts, beech mast, chestnuts and acorns, when in season, and haws, pine seeds, young shoots and bark. Some species eat insects and snails and occasionally take bird eggs and nestlings. The garden dormouse is more carnivorous than other species and preys on smaller mammals such as shrews.

Breeding

Mating takes place very soon after the dormice emerge from hibernation and offspring are produced after a gestation of 23–24 days. The young, of which there are usually three to five, are born in a nest of about 6 inches (15 cm) in diameter, twice the size of the ordinary sleeping nests. These nursery nests are frequently constructed in holes in trees, and are lined with hair and feathers. When the local dormouse population is high, making nesting space scarce, several females may share a single hole. At first the young dormice are naked and blind. Fur grows at 13 days but it is molted and replaced 5 days later, when the eyes open. The young become independent at 40 days old. There are two or more litters in a year.

Food for the feast

The Romans reared edible dormice in enclosed plantations of oak, walnut and chestnut trees, known as *gliraria*. To fatten the dormice, they were kept in small earthenware pots called *dolia*, which left them with only enough room to perform the movements of eating. A dormouse just before hibernating will eat virtually anything put in front of it, and an obese, bloated dormouse was considered a great delicacy. Dormice became status symbols among wealthy Romans, who even had the dormice weighed in front of the dinner guests. This ancient custom has given rise to the species' common names of the fat or edible dormouse.

The edible dormouse usually chooses holes in trees as nesting sites. If disturbed, the female carries her young to another site, usually under the cover of darkness.

DORMOUSE POSSUM

PREVIOUSLY KNOWN AS dormouse phalangers, dormouse possums are small, agile marsupials that grow up to 1 foot (30 cm) in length, half of which may be accounted for by the tail. As their name suggests, dormouse possums resemble the unrelated Eurasian dormice of the family Gliridae. They have a pointed muzzle, large eyes and thin, almost naked, ears. The body is stout and covered with dense, soft fur. However, the tail is not as bushy as that of the true dormice. It is prehensile and is used as an extra support in tree climbing.

Deep sleep

Dormouse possums live in wooded country in Australia, including Tasmania, and New Guinea. They are usually active at night, but sometimes also emerge on cloudy days. During the day, dormouse possums lie up in nests, and several may live together. Some nests are inside tree holes and abandoned bird nests. Others are made of soft bark fibers and are built by the dormouse possums themselves. They may travel ¼ mile (400 m) to find suitable nest materials. If the wood is rotten, a dormouse possum can excavate its own hole. One individual was found in a cavity 2 feet (60 cm) deep.

When sleeping in their nests, dormouse possums curl up in a ball with their noses against their chests, ears folded and tails curled in a tight coil under them. They can be picked up and handled without waking, although they may make a quiet hissing noise on being touched. Their deep sleep recalls the hibernation of true dormice, and experiments have shown that when they enter such deep sleep, dormouse possums are in a state of torpor.

A sleeping dormouse possum feels cold to the touch, and measurements of its body temperature show that it is the same or even less than the air temperature. The animal may take 3 hours or more to awaken after its sleep. In one study the arousal period in *Burramys* averaged just over 19 hours. As the dormouse possum awakens, its body temperature rises, slowly at first, then more rapidly until the normal level of about 90° F (32° C) is reached.

The deep sleep of dormouse possums is not true hibernation like that of true dormice, which in the hazel dormouse, *Muscardinus avellanarius*, lasts from October to April in the British Isles. A dormouse possum never has any prolonged period of sleep: it is alternately active and dormant for a few days at a time. In the summer months it is more active and in the winter more dormant, but activity is not related to air temperature. Dormouse possums may be quite active in cold weather, but spend more than half their time asleep in the winter months, from March to August in Australia.

Dormouse possums feed on a wide range of foods, including flower nectar and pollen, insects and scorpions. Pictured is Cercartetus lepidus, *feeding on eucalyptus flowers.*

Acrobatic hunters

Dormouse possums are energetic hunters, chasing insects and other small animals in the trees. They catch lizards up to 6 inches (15 cm) long and eat them tail first, leaving only the scales and claws. Moths are seized in the forepaws while they are in flight and are eaten after the wings have been removed. Dormouse possums also feed on other insects, such as cicadas, mantises, bugs and beetles, and on spiders.

Beetle larvae are eaten with great care. First the hind end of the abdomen is bitten off and the intestine is gripped in the front teeth, pulled out and discarded. The dormouse possum then devours the rest of the body, apart from the tough skin. Other foods include fruits, nuts, leaves, pollen and nectar. When insects become scarce with the approach of winter, dormouse

DORMOUSE POSSUMS

CLASS	**Mammalia**
ORDER	**Marsupialia**
FAMILY	**Burramyidae**
GENUS	***Cercartetus*** **(detailed below),** ***Distoechurus, Acrobates*** **and** ***Burramys***
SPECIES	**Several, including** *C. concinnus;* *C. nanus; C. lepidus;* **and** *C. caudatus*

ALTERNATIVE NAMES
Dormouse phalanger; dormouse opossum; pygmy possum; pygmy opossum

WEIGHT
Up to about 1 oz. (28 g)

LENGTH
Head and body: 2¾–4¾ in. (7–12 cm); tail: 2¾–7 in. (7–18 cm)

DISTINCTIVE FEATURES
Large eyes; pointed muzzle; small digits with distinct pads; long, prehensile tail, well furred at base but otherwise scantily haired

DIET
Flower nectar and pollen, fruits, nuts, leaves, insects, spiders, scorpions and small lizards

BREEDING
Age at first breeding: 15 months (*C. caudatus*); breeding season: all year; number of young: usually 5 (*C. concinnus, C. nanus, C. lepida*), 1 to 4 (*C. caudatus*); gestation period: not known; breeding interval: 2 litters per year (*C. caudatus*)

LIFE SPAN
Up to 8 years in captivity, much less in wild

HABITAT
Forest, heaths and scrubland

DISTRIBUTION
New Guinea; southern and eastern Australia

STATUS
Locally common; *C. caudatus*: scarce

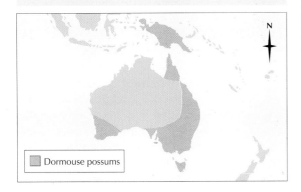

Dormouse possums

possums store up fat, mainly in their tails. This behavior, which is shared with the true dormice, helps tide them over the lean period.

Little is known of the breeding habits of dormouse possums. The pouches of females contain four to six teats and up to six young have been found in a litter. Some species of dormouse possum probably breed twice in a year.

Rare species rediscovered

In August 1966, a small possum was caught in a ski lodge in the Victorian Alps, 130 miles (210 km) northeast of Melbourne, Australia. Zoologists realized that it was the burramys, *Burramys parvus*, also known as the mountain pygmy possum. Fossils of the burramys dating back 15,000 years were first described in 1896. The fossils had been found in caves in southeastern Australia and were thought to provide a link between the kangaroos and the Phalangeridae, the family to which dormouse possums were assigned at the time. Later, improved methods of examination revealed that the burramys is a species of dormouse possum.

The burramys is currently regarded as threatened. More than a century of vegetation modification brought about by burning and grazing has adversely affected the local environment and, consequently, burramys numbers. More recently, ski resort development has caused the destruction and fragmentation of the species' natural habitat. Increased erosion and aridity have interrupted the species' breeding and hibernation patterns. The introduction of non-native species that prey on the burramys, such as the red fox, *Vulpes vulpes*, has also reduced numbers. As a result of all these factors, the adult burramys population has decreased to about 3,000 animals.

Dormouse possums (Cercartetus nanus, above) often make their nests in holes in trees. They are primarily nocturnal and sleep in their nests during the day.

DOTTEREL

THE EURASIAN DOTTEREL IS A small shorebird in the plover family, Charadriidae. It has a striking plumage, but is usually inconspicuous as its gray-brown upperparts merge with the ground. Its cheeks and throat are whitish, and there is a prominent white stripe through the eye. The breast is chestnut below and grayish brown above, the two colors separated by a white band. The belly is black. In winter the dotterel becomes a paler, more uniform brown, while the white stripes through the eye and across the breast become less distinct.

An Ice Age castaway?

Although it belongs to the shorebirds, the Eurasian dotterel is very rarely found near the shore. It breeds in widely scattered inland localities in Europe, Asia and, occasionally, North America, but is most abundant in northern Scandinavia and Siberia. In North America the dotterel's status is that of a rare and sporadic breeder in parts of northwestern Alaska. In Europe and Asia the dotterel's breeding range includes two habitat types: northern tundra, often at low altitudes, and, to the south, alpine moors and meadows in high mountains.

The Eurasian dotterel's summer distribution around the Arctic tundra and in the mountainous areas of temperate Europe and Asia recalls the distribution of certain alpine plants. These plants were adapted to harsh growing conditions and during the Ice Age flourished throughout Europe. When the glaciers retreated the plants were left stranded on mountaintops, where the climate remained suitably harsh and "Arctic." It may be that at one time the dotterel was also widespread in Europe, and that with the end of the Ice Age most of its populations followed the retreating ice to the Arctic, leaving small, isolated populations further south in high mountains. This theory, however, cannot be proved. Some ornithologists think that the Eurasian dotterel was originally a mountain bird and that the species has only recently spread to Arctic regions.

Migrates in small groups

When the breeding season is over, dotterels migrate southward in small parties. Their wintering grounds are in the plains of northern and southern Spain, North Africa and the Middle East. At this time of year dotterels inhabit farmland and semidesert.

Despite being birds of cold and desolate places, Eurasian dotterels bred on the reclaimed polders of the Zuider Zee in the Netherlands in 1961–1969. The species was first found to be nesting there in 1961, when several nests were discovered in crops of flax and peas.

Insect eater

The Eurasian dotterel eats mainly insects, chiefly the beetles and flies that thrive in the summer on its nesting grounds. While migrating, the dotterel also takes earthworms, spiders and small mollusks. It feeds on the ground, searching through vegetation or probing among roots for hidden larvae.

Breeds near the snow

Dotterels start breeding before the snow has completely melted, choosing nesting sites around the edges of the slowly retreating ice fields. The female, slightly brighter in color, seems to take the initiative. The pair of birds chase one another over the ground, pecking at each other and jumping into the air.

The nest, built by the male alone, is a depression about 3½ inches (9 cm) across, lined with fragments of leaves and lichen. The usual clutch is two or three eggs, laid at 1-day intervals. Although both birds have a bare brood patch on the belly, incubation is carried out by the male, with only occasional assistance from the female.

Unlike most birds, male dotterels (below) incubate the eggs and care for the chicks. They are paler and better camouflaged than the females, which play a dominant role in courtship.

EURASIAN DOTTEREL

CLASS	**Aves**
ORDER	**Charadriiformes**
FAMILY	**Charadriidae**
GENUS AND SPECIES	*Charadrius morinellus*

WEIGHT
3–4½ oz. (90–130 g)

LENGTH
Head to tail: 8–8½ in. (20–22 cm); wingspan: 22–25 in. (56–64 cm)

DISTINCTIVE FEATURES
Fairly long legs; mainly grayish brown with bold white eyestripe, chestnut breast and black belly; female brighter than male but both sexes have dull plumage in winter

DIET
Mainly invertebrates such as beetles, flies, spiders and earthworms; some plant matter

BREEDING
Age at first breeding: 1 year; breeding season: May–July; number of eggs: usually 2 or 3; incubation period: 24–28 days; fledging period: 25–30 days; breeding interval: 1 year

LIFE SPAN
Probably up to 10 years

HABITAT
Summer: Arctic tundra, alpine moors and meadows. Winter and while on migration: semidesert, farmland and other open areas.

DISTRIBUTION
Summer: northern Scotland, Scandinavia and Siberia, high mountains of southern and central Europe and (occasionally) parts of northwestern Alaska. Winter: parts of Spain, North Africa and Middle East.

STATUS
Generally common: Scandinavia and Siberia; scarce: rest of Europe; rare: Alaska

Eurasian dotterel ■ summer ■ winter

When migrating the Eurasian dotterel (female, above) often stops on arable farmland to rest and feed.

He may even push her off the nest before she has finished laying the full clutch. Sometimes the female dotterel mates with two males and lays a clutch of eggs in each of their nests. Incubation takes about 3–4 weeks, and the young are active shortly after hatching.

The male dotterel looks after the chicks, sheltering them from the rain and calling to warn them to crouch quietly if danger threatens. The female does not desert her family but stays nearby, giving the alarm when necessary. The young are fully fledged within a month, and the family splits up to join other dotterels in flocks of up to 20, which are known as trips.

Daft dotterel

The reaction of shorebirds to humans goes from extreme to extreme through the year. Outside the breeding season they are very wary, taking flight as soon as anyone comes into sight. For many people a shorebird is never more than a brown flash, streaking away with rapid wingbeats to the accompaniment of a whistling alarm call. On the other hand, during the breeding season, some shorebirds behave in an apparently rash manner. It is possible to walk right up to their nests before they take flight, and even then they are likely to return and attempt to lure the intruder away from the nest by pretending to have a broken wing. This is known as a distraction display.

The Eurasian dotterel is as fearless as any and in Scotland the term "daft dotterel" was once used for someone who acts stupidly. For this is the impression that a dotterel gives as it sits firmly on its nest in the path of a herd of deer or flock of sheep. It is usual for well-camouflaged species of ground-nesting bird to sit motionless on their eggs in the hope that predators will not see them. This strategy is highly successful but is not without risk: by not fleeing when a predator is nearby, the sitting bird places both itself and its valuable clutch of eggs in danger.

DRAGONET

Generally dragonets are inconspicuous fish. Males of the species Callionymus lyra *have brightly colored spots and stripes, but despite these markings still blend into the seabed.*

DRAGONETS ARE LONG, bottom-living fish that range from coastal shallows to deep waters in tropical and temperate seas. They are 4½–12 inches (11.5–30 cm) long, scaleless and have a flattish belly and rounded back. The head is oblong and flattened, with large eyes set close together on the top. The mouth can be pushed outward and has large lips at the end of the snout. The pelvic fins are widely separated and are well forward on the throat. The pectoral fins are large and have two to three free rays, which are organs of touch. The long dorsal and anal fins are larger in the male than in the female, and the front part of the male's dorsal fin has a very long leading spine. Dragonets camouflage themselves by wriggling into gravel, stones and sand on the seabed.

The male of the European species *Callionymus lyra* is so different in appearance from the female that the two were once thought to belong to different species. The supposed species were called the gemmeous dragonet and the sordid dragonet, the latter referring to the female. The male *Callionymus lyra* is yellow to brown on the back and orange on the flanks and underside. The whole body is tinged with azure-blue spots and stripes. The dorsal and pectoral fins are large and marked with bright blue spots and whirls; the pelvic fins are dark blue and the eyes blue green. The female *Callionymus lyra* is brown with a white underside and smaller fins. In Medieval English the term dragonet was used to refer to the baby dragons of legend. The name was not applied to the fish of the family Callionymidae until the 18th century.

Scientists have recently become aware of two new species of dragonet. *Callionymus leucopoecilus* is found in the Yellow Sea, between China and Korea. It has four spines in its first dorsal fin and nine rays each in the second dorsal and anal fins. *Foetorepus goodenbeani* occurs in the western North Atlantic. Both sexes have a second dorsal fin featuring a number of yellow circles with olive brown margins (male) or rows of yellow marks (female).

Built-in suction pump

Dragonets feed on worms, small crustaceans and mollusks on the sea floor at depths of 165–330 feet (50–100 m). Despite the position of their eyes, high on the head, dragonets pay little attention to anything that swims in the water column above them.

A dragonet is not built for speed, though with its large pectoral fins it can dart forward suddenly. Otherwise its movements are leisurely and are mainly limited to skimming just over the bottom and resting at frequent intervals with the head slightly raised.

Bottom-living fish such as dragonets are at a disadvantage in their breathing compared with those species that swim freely. A fish that is constantly moving needs only to open its mouth for water to flow in and across the gills. A dragonet has only a small opening to the gills. Its gill cavity and the associated bones and muscles are so constructed that water is forced through by a bellows action of the gill covers. The fish opens its mouth and the suction pump of the gill chamber enables it to breathe.

DRAGONETS

CLASS	**Osteichthyes**
ORDER	**Perciformes**
FAMILY	**Callionymidae**
GENUS	**18, including *Callionymus*, *Calliurichthys* and *Repomucenus***
SPECIES	**130, including *Callionymus lyra***

WEIGHT
Up to 9 oz. (250 g)

LENGTH
Up to 10 in. (25 cm), most species usually less than 4 in. (10 cm)

DISTINCTIVE FEATURES
Elongated, scaleless body; flattish head and belly; rounded back; large eyes set on top of head; long dorsal and anal fins; coloration usually matches seabed but bright spots, stripes or whirls in some species

DIET
Mainly bottom-living worms, crustaceans and mollusks

BREEDING
Age at first breeding: 1 year (*Repomucenus valenciennei*), 3–5 years (*Callionymus lyra*); breeding season: peaks in spring and autumn (*R. valenciennei, Calliurichthys japonicus*); breeding interval: 1 or 2 years

LIFE SPAN
Up to 7 years

HABITAT
Shallow waters up to 330 ft. (100 m) deep, with sandy seabeds

DISTRIBUTION
Mainly Indian Ocean and western Pacific; *Callionymus lyra*: temperate seas

STATUS
Most species common or locally common; 15 species critically endangered

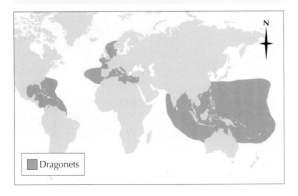

Dragonets

Colorful courtship

In *Callionymus lyra* the breeding season is from February to June or even later, and spawning takes place close inshore. The brilliance of the male's colors peaks in spring and summer, during courtship. Prior to mating, the male approaches the female with all of his fins spread wide. The dorsal fin, normally laid back along the body, is fully erect. As the final movement in the courtship ritual, the male points his mouth downward and pushes his upper lip forward, nodding to the female. Once the female has accepted him, he places his pelvic fin under hers and together they swim steeply upward toward the upper layers of the water. When they near the surface, their position changes slightly so that the anal fins of the partners lie side by side, forming a gutter into which eggs and sperm are shed. This keeps them together long enough for the eggs to be fertilized.

The fertilized eggs are small, less than 0.8 millimeters in diameter, and have a honeycomb pattern. Soon after they are laid, the eggs float to the surface. They hatch in 2 weeks and the young fish remain near the surface, moving to the bottom during the following winter.

Males mate only once

The age of a fish can often be told by examining the growth rings on the otoliths (ear bones) or on the vertebrae or other bones. In dragonets the most reliable method of determining age is to look for the growth rings in certain bones of the shoulder girdle, known as the second radials. Scientists have discovered from these that the males grow quickly but live for no longer than 5 years. The females grow more slowly and do not reach as large a size as the males, 8 inches (20 cm) as opposed to 12 inches (30 cm) for males.

Dragonets live on the seabed and only rise to the upper waters of the sea during courtship. They hide by wriggling into sand and gravel.

DRAGONFLY

Nearly all dragonflies lay their eggs in water. The female inserts her eggs into water plants or (above) releases them so that they sink to the bottom.

DRAGONFLIES ARE COLORFUL, POWERFUL fliers and are among the fastest of all insects in the air. Most dragonflies are large and hold their wings stiffly extended on each side when at rest, whereas other insects generally fold them over the back. The wings are capable of only simple up-and-down movement. There is no coupling device joining the front and back wings, as in butterflies and advanced moths, and there is a fine network of "veins" supporting the wing membrane. These characteristics suggest that dragonflies are primitive insects that have existed with little change for a very long time. The earliest known fossil dragonflies are from the late Carboniferous period, and were deposited about 300 million years ago. Dragonflies similar to those living today were alive in the Jurassic period, 150 million years ago, when dinosaurs were on the earth.

The name dragonfly is frequently used to stand as an equivalent of the insect order Odonata. However, the members of the suborder Zygoptera (the damselflies) are very distinct in appearance and are discussed elsewhere.

Living dragonflies consist of two suborders, the Anisoptera, which contains all the familiar species, and the Anisozygoptera. Scientists are aware of only two species in this latter suborder; one is native to Japan and the other is native to the Himalaya Mountains.

As in their relatives the damselflies, dragonflies usually have transparent, colorless wings but these may be tinted or patterned, and the body is often brightly colored. Males are generally more dramatically colored than females. They differ markedly from damselflies in having a swift, powerful flight. Estimates of their actual speed are difficult to obtain and vary from 35 miles per hour (56 km/h) up to 60 miles per hour (96 km/h). Dragonflies' antennae are minute but the eyes are enormous in comparison, occupying the greater part of the head. Each compound eye may contain as many as 30,000 facets.

Aerial patrols

Dragonflies fly patrols over a fixed area. They are most often seen near water, which is where they breed, although their powerful flight carries them far away from their breeding places, and they may frequently be seen resting in trees and on bushes. Dragonflies often fly back and forth over a specific area, landing on one of a small number of resting places. The area that the dragonflies patrol may have been selected as suitable for hunting prey or, especially if the area is over water, it may be the territory chosen by a male dragonfly, which will then mate with any female of its own species that flies into this area. These males defend their territories strenuously

against other males of the same species. After a while they begin to show evidence of the confrontations they have experienced, in the shape of torn wings and mutilated legs. Whether hunting or fighting, the sense employed most often by dragonflies is that of sight. A dragonfly can detect movement up to 40 feet (12 m) away.

Some species of dragonflies are migratory and may fly great distances over land and sea. Two of these species, *Sympetrum flaveolum* and *S. fonscolombei*, sometimes visit Britain from Europe. The British population of another species, *Aeshna mixta*, is probably regularly reinforced by newcomers from continental Europe.

Unlike damselflies, dragonflies have large, powerful wings and are among the fastest of all flying insects.

DRAGONFLIES

PHYLUM **Arthropoda**

CLASS **Insecta**

ORDER **Odonata**

SUBORDER **Anisoptera and Anisozygoptera**

FAMILY **Aeshnidae; Gomphidae; others**

GENUS AND SPECIES **Many**

ALTERNATIVE NAME
Horse-stinger

LENGTH
Body: up to 6 in. (15 cm); wingspan: up to 7½ in. (19 cm)

DISTINCTIVE FEATURES
Long, slender body; 2 pairs of wings, rear pair more broadly based than front pair; intricate network of veins on wings; at rest wings held flat and at right angles to body; very large eyes that meet in middle

DIET
Adult: small insects, especially gnats and mosquitoes. Larva: midge larvae and other small, aquatic invertebrates; small fish.

BREEDING
Larval period: 2–5 years (temperate regions), usually several months (Tropics)

LIFE SPAN
Adult: up to 10 years in Tropics, elsewhere usually several years

HABITAT
Many aquatic habitats, including ponds, lakes, marshes, rivers, ditches and streams

DISTRIBUTION
Virtually worldwide

STATUS
Many species common; at least 110 species threatened

A dragonfly's large compound eyes are sensitive to even the slightest movement. Each may feature over 30,000 facets, or ommatidia, more than any other insect.

One dragonfly species, *Libellula quadrimaculata*, sometimes migrates in spectacular swarms. In 1862 a swarm of this species was observed in Germany, estimated at nearly 2.5 thousand million strong, and in June 1900 a huge swarm appeared in the sky over Antwerp, Belgium. In 1947 a large migration of another species, *Sympetrum striolatum*, was observed on the southern coast of Ireland.

Masked nymphs

Dragonflies are predatory in all stages of development. The adults catch other insects on the wing, seizing them with their forwardly directed legs and chewing them with their powerful jaws. In the southeastern United States two large species, *Anax junius* and *Coryphaeshna ingens*, are leading predators of honeybees.

The larvae, or nymphs, capture their prey using what is known as a mask, a mechanism that is shared with the damselflies but is otherwise unique among insects. The enlarged labium or lower lip is armed with a pair of hooks. At rest it is folded under the head, but it is extensible and can be shot out in front of the head, the hooks being used to seize the prey like a pair of pincers. The victim is then drawn back within reach of the jaws. Dragonfly larvae also prey on other insects, tadpoles and small fish, and those

of the larger species can considerably reduce the numbers of young fish in a rearing pond. However, young dragonfly larvae also perform a useful ecological service by destroying great numbers of the aquatic larvae of mosquitoes.

The flying tandem

The mating procedure for dragonflies and damselflies is very similar. The male transfers his sperm from the primary sexual organ near the tip of his abdomen to an accessory organ farther forward, at the base of the abdomen. He then alights on the back of a female and curls his abdomen under his own body in order to seize her head, not the thorax as in damselflies, with a pair of claspers at the end of his abdomen. He releases the hold with his legs but continues to grasp his mate with the claspers. The female then curls her abdomen around in such a way that the tip of it makes contact with the male accessory organ. Both before and after mating the two may fly together, with the female held by the male claspers, in what is known as the tandem position. They may even maintain this position while the eggs are being laid.

Dragonflies almost always lay their eggs in water, using one of two methods. Some, including the large hawker dragonflies of the genus *Aeshna*, insert their eggs into the stems of water plants, as damselflies do. Others, such as the golden-ringed dragonfly, *Cordulegaster boltoni*, force their eggs into the sand or gravel at the margins of shallow streams. This second method is seen in most British species. They fly close over the water's surface and repeatedly dip the tip of the body into the water, extruding eggs at the same time, which then sink to the bottom.

Jet-propelled insects

Nearly all dragonflies, and all British species, spend their early life underwater. The nymphs vary in shape. Those that live in mud are short, thick-set and covered with a dense coat of hairs to which the mud clings. When these larvae are at rest, only the eyes and the tip of the abdomen are exposed, the rest being buried. Golden-ringed dragonflies have larvae of this type. Those species that live among waterweed are more slender and active, though no dragonfly larvae are as delicate as those of damselflies.

Dragonfly larvae have gills inside the intestine a short distance from their hind opening, and they breathe by drawing water into the rectum and then driving it out again. This mechanism is also used for another purpose: if it is disturbed, a dragonfly larva drives the water out forcibly, thereby propelling itself rapidly forward, in a simple form of jet propulsion.

When the larva is fully grown, a period of 2 years or more in most European species, it crawls up a plant growing in the water. It climbs until it is above the water's surface where it undergoes its final molt to metamorphose into an adult dragonfly.

Dragonfly predators

The increasing worldwide destruction of their habitat by pollution, drainage, dredging and infilling of ponds is the most serious threat to dragonflies. As larvae, their chief natural enemies are fish, the young of which are themselves preyed upon by well-grown dragonfly larvae. In fact, dragonfly larvae probably form an important source of food for freshwater fish. When the larvae are small, they are also eaten by other predatory insects, including larger dragonfly larvae, often of their own species. The adults are so swift and active that they have few natural enemies, but several small birds of prey, including the hobby, *Falco subbuteo*, feed extensively on them. In the tropical countries of East Asia dragonflies were at one time caught with sticks smeared with a form of bird lime and eaten fried in oil.

Prehistoric giants

The present-day Odonata are among the largest living insects. In tropical America there are damselflies with bodies 5 inches (12.5 cm) long and wings spanning 7 inches (18 cm). These are slender, fragile creatures and are greatly exceeded in bulk by the Borneo dragonfly, *Tetracanthagyna plagiata*, which also has a wingspan of 7 inches and a body measuring about 5 inches in length. No modern dragonflies, however, compare in size with some that lived in forests 300 million years ago. At Commentry, France, fossil remains of these species have been found, including impressions of wings, which show that the wingspan of the largest prehistoric species, *Meganeuramonyi*, was as much as 27 inches (69 cm), similar to that of a crow. They are by far the largest insects known to have lived on the earth, although no larval remains have been uncovered so far.

Many male dragonflies (A. cyanea, below) are brightly colored. Females generally have less striking colors.

DRONGO

Most drongo species are noisy and several, such as the lesser racket-tailed drongo, are also skillful voice mimics.

THERE ARE 24 SPECIES OF DRONGO, which are medium-sized birds measuring 7–15 inches (18–38 cm) in length. They have long wings tapering to a point and long tails that are often forked, curled or with long, trailing flags. The usual plumage color is blackish with a marked green, blue or purplish gloss to some areas, but two species are pale gray. The legs and heavy bill are black, the eyes usually red and there are conspicuous bristles around the nostrils. The relationship of drongos to other birds is not known. It has variously been suggested that they are related to flycatchers, crows and shrikes.

Drongos are found in tropical Africa, including Madagascar, the oriental regions of Asia and eastward to the Solomon Islands and southeastern Australia. Although they are familiar birds, little is known of their habits. Even the black drongo, or king crow, *Dicrurus macrocercus*, which is one of the most common birds of India and Malaysia, has received little attention from field ornithologists. Most drongos are best known for their ornate plumage. Glossy plumage patterns distinguish the various species. The spangled drongo, *D. hottentottus*, is named after the glossy spangles, or spots, on its breast and neck. It has an ornate forked tail, and the

outer tail feathers curl. The tail of the greater racket-tailed drongo, *D. paradiseus*, features two outer feathers that extend 1 foot (30 cm) beyond the rest of the tail. This is nearly twice the length of the blackbird-sized head and body. For most of their length these feathers consist of only the shaft, but there is a twisted flag, or racket, of vanes at the tip. Some drongos have small crests of dense feathers springing from the base of the bill and curling over the crown of the head.

Vocal skills

Drongos are colorful birds and are relatively easy to see and identify, but they usually live in dense forest or in thickets and shrubberies and are therefore hard to study in life. They are not, however, shy. In fact, drongos are renowned for their aggressiveness, especially during the breeding season. They are also inquisitive, often following humans rather than flying away. Many drongos also attract attention because they are noisy, some having harsh calls, others producing striking songs. Both the greater racket-tailed drongo and the lesser racket-tailed drongo, *D. remifer*, are good voice mimics.

Drongos are prominent in the mixed flocks of small birds that fly through tropical woodlands and forests in search of food. They seek large insects such as moths, wasps, bees, beetles and dragonflies. Drongos appear to have a preference for wasps and bees, sometimes picking them out of swarms. It seems that the bright warning coloration typical of these insects, which deters most other animals from eating them, conveys no such message to drongos.

At other times drongos follow cattle, deer and troops of monkeys to catch the insects that they stir up. They perch on the backs of cattle and deer and warn them, by flying up and calling, of impending danger. Drongos also perch on bare branches and telephone wires, flying out after insects and returning to the perch with their prey, in the manner of flycatchers. However, drongos are by no means wholly insectivorous. Some, for instance the spangled drongo, often feed on flower nectar and fruits.

Fragile-looking nests

Drongos lay two to four eggs in a frail-looking nest that appears to be too small for the bird that made it. The nest is basket-shaped, constructed of fibers and grass stems bound by cobwebs, and is usually slung from a forked branch high in a tree. From the few observations made, it seems that the females sit on the eggs more than the

SPANGLED DRONGO

CLASS	**Aves**
ORDER	**Passeriformes**
FAMILY	**Dicruridae**
GENUS AND SPECIES	***Dicrurus hottentottus***

ALTERNATIVE NAME
Hair-crested drongo

LENGTH
Head to tail: about 12½ in. (32 cm)

DISTINCTIVE FEATURES
Fairly long, slightly decurved bill; broad tail with twisted fork in center; hairlike crest; plumage mainly black with greenish gloss and paler spangles (spots) on breast and neck

DIET
Mainly large insects, fruits and flower nectar

BREEDING
Age at first breeding: probably 1 year; breeding season: March–August; number of eggs: usually 2 to 4; incubation period: not known; fledging period: not known; breeding interval: 1 year

LIFE SPAN
Not known

HABITAT
Evergreen and moist deciduous forest, often in association with flowering trees

DISTRIBUTION
India east to southern China and south through Southeast Asia to Australia

STATUS
Locally common

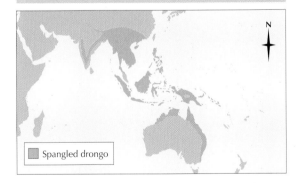

Spangled drongo

males, and that both parents feed the chicks. Drongos defend their nests actively. The parents ignore small, harmless birds but any hawks, owls, crows and hornbills that venture near to the nest are aggressively attacked and relentlessly driven away.

Small forest birds often take advantage of the aggressive behavior exhibited by drongos and nest in the vicinity of a breeding pair. They themselves go about their nesting duties unmolested and they are protected from many predators by the vigorous defense tactics adopted by the nesting drongos. However, drongos still fall victim to nest parasitism. Both the Indian cuckoo, *Cuculus micropterus*, and the koel, *Eudynamys scolopacea*, regularly lay their eggs in the nests of the black drongo, greater racket-tailed drongo and ashy drongo, *D. leucophaeus*.

Change of place, change of plumage

The plumage of a drongo species often varies from place to place and the changes in plumage can be followed closely. This is most useful to zoologists, for whereas in mammals changes in form have been preserved in fossil records, such as the changes from early horses to modern horses, well-preserved fossil remains of birds are less common. Patterns of change are therefore more easily studied in living groups.

It is possible to show gradual variations of characteristics from one end of the drongos' range to the other. For instance, within some species the average wing length decreases from the Himalayas southward to Sri Lanka and Malaysia. Similarly, the degree to which the tails of spangled drongos curl varies across the Malay Archipelago. The racket-tailed drongos lack a crest in some parts of their respective ranges, but possess one of more than 2 inches (5 cm) in others. Moreover, atmospheric humidity has a discernable effect on the gloss of the drongos' plumage. In humid regions drongos tend to have a rich, deep blue or purplish gloss to their feathers, but in dry regions their plumage is more often tinged green.

The black drongo lives in more open country than other drongos, such as in fields and along roadsides. It eats large quantities of insects considered to be agricultural pests and feeds on insects stirred up by cattle.

DUCKS, GEESE AND SWANS

DUCKS, GEESE AND SWANS form a relatively small but varied group of waterbirds. They have evolved a variety of adaptations for swimming or wading, although many species regularly breed and feed away from wetlands and marine habitats. The largest species is the trumpeter swan, *Cygnus buccinator,* which reaches 33 pounds (15 kg), making it one of the world's heaviest flying birds. In Eurasia this species is replaced by its close relative, the whooper swan, *C. cygnus.* At the other end of the scale is the white pygmy goose, *Nettapus coromandelianus,* which weighs no more than 7¾ ounces (220 g), about the same as a dove.

Classification

Ducks, geese and swans belong to the order Anseriformes, and are represented worldwide. There are 144 species, which are collectively known as wildfowl, or waterfowl. Together they comprise the family Anatidae. Within this family are three subfamilies: Anseranatinae, the sole member of which is the Australian magpie goose, *Anseranas semipalmata;* Anserinae, which includes the swans and true geese; and Anatinae, which contains the true ducks. The three remaining species of birds in the order Anseriformes are confined to South America and are placed in a separate family, the Anhimidae, or screamers.

The taxonomy of the Anseriformes is highly complex. Several species and genera of ducks, geese and swans display mixed characteristics that relate them to more than one tribe within the order. Moreover the familiar terms duck and goose are not strictly scientific because they do not correspond

The black swan, Cygnus atratus, *of Australia, is one of three swans found in the Southern Hemisphere.*

with the order's taxonomic divisions. Some birds known as geese, including the three species of pygmy geese in the tropical genus *Nettapus* and the five sheldgeese species in the South American genus *Chloephaga,* are more closely related to most ducks than to true geese, and are therefore classified in the subfamily Anatinae. Conversely, the Australian freckled duck, *Stictonetta naevosa,* and the nine species of whistling ducks in the genus *Dendrocygna* have less in common with true ducks than they do with swans and true geese, and are thus placed in the subfamily Anserinae.

Sometimes the term "duck" is used to refer to the female alone, the corresponding term for the male being "drake." For example, it is correct to say that "the drake American ring-necked duck, *Aythya collaris,* has a much brighter plumage than the duck." However, it is almost always possible to determine the intended meaning from the context.

CLASSIFICATION
CLASS Aves
ORDER Anseriformes
FAMILY Anatidae: wildfowl; Anhimidae: screamers
NUMBER OF SPECIES Subfamily Anseranatinae: 1; Subfamily Anserinae: 33; Subfamily Anatinae: 111

Ducks, Geese and Swans Family Tree

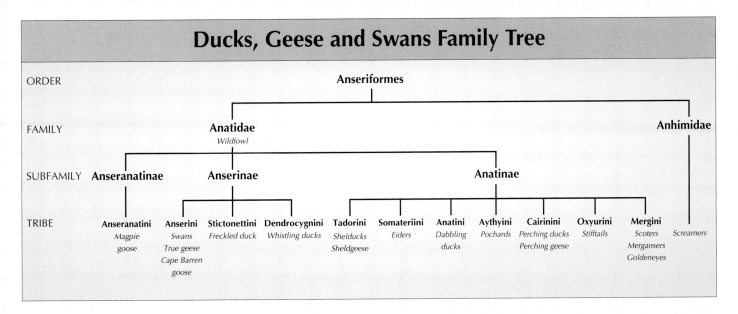

ORDER				Anseriformes								
FAMILY		**Anatidae** *Wildfowl*										**Anhimidae**
SUBFAMILY	**Anseranatinae**	**Anserinae**			**Anatinae**							
TRIBE	**Anseranatini** *Magpie goose*	**Anserini** *Swans True geese Cape Barren goose*	**Stictonettini** *Freckled duck*	**Dendrocygnini** *Whistling ducks*	**Tadorini** *Shelducks Sheldgeese*	**Somateriini** *Eiders*	**Anatini** *Dabbling ducks*	**Aythyini** *Pochards*	**Cairinini** *Perching ducks Perching geese*	**Oxyurini** *Stifftails*	**Mergini** *Scoters Mergansers Goldeneyes*	*Screamers*

Physical adaptations

Ducks, geese and swans share a range of morphological features. Three of the toes are linked by webbing, to serve as paddles and to provide support on soft ground. The legs are positioned well back on the body, to maximize forward power and steering efficiency when swimming. The neck is relatively long; in predatory species this design assists in catching prey, in vegetarian species it facilitates the grazing of plants on the ground or at the bottom of fresh water. The bill is strong, blunt and shaped like a spatula, with a horny nail at the tip.

Wildfowl swim well but due to their rear-set legs they walk with an ungainly waddle on land and have difficulty in taking off. To get airborne from water, ducks, geese and swans must gain speed by running along the surface while flapping hard with their wings. This procedure takes several seconds in the heavier species of swans and geese, such as the trumpeter swan and the mute swan, *Cygnus olor*, of Eurasia. A notable exception is provided by the teal, *Anas crecca*, which is able to take off almost vertically, an adaptation to fleeing danger in relatively enclosed marshes where there is little advance warning of the approach of predators.

The Arctic summer provides a short-lived abundance of food for geese. Snow geese fly north to their breeding grounds in Alaska and Canada in huge flocks, returning with their young just 3 months later.

plumage during the flightless part of their molt they would be extremely vulnerable to predators, particularly foxes, cats and birds of prey. Therefore in male wildfowl the first stage of the molt is to rapidly grow dull feathers for camouflage. Thus protected, the flight feathers are renewed. The temporary dull feathers are subsequently replaced with new bright ones. The short-lived dull plumage is known as the eclipse plumage.

Three of the four species of South American steamer ducks, *Tachyeres brachypterus*, *T. pteneres* and *T. leucocephalus*, have lost the power of flight altogether. All are sea ducks. The fourth species of steamer duck, *T. patachonicus*, has retained its ability to fly.

The smallest true goose, the red-breasted goose, Branta ruficollis, *breeds in the treeless Siberian tundra, where its nest is visible from afar. It gains protection from Arctic foxes by nesting close to the peregrine falcon,* Falco peregrinus.

A unique family

The three screamers bear a superficial resemblance to geese, but have a unique body structure because they are the least aquatic of all the Anseriformes. Screamers have a turkey-shaped body and bill, proportionately long legs, barely webbed feet and two spurs on the leading edge of each wing. They are the only living birds to lack hooked protuberances on the ribs for supporting the rib cage.

Screamers share an unusual feather arrangement with the penguins: their feathers are all of similar structure and grow evenly all over the body. In the vast majority of birds, including wildfowl, feathers are of several types and grow in distinct tracts called pterylae. These fan out to cover any bare areas, giving the outward appearance of uniformity.

Waterproof feathers

Ducks, geese and swans must carefully maintain their plumage to retain its waterproof qualities. This is achieved by daily preening and by molting. Ducks molt twice a year, while geese and swans have a single annual molt. Except for two species of geese, wildfowl molt all of the flight feathers of the wings at once, and are flightless for a period of 3–4 weeks. The magpie goose and the ruddy-headed goose, *Chloephaga rubidiceps*, are exceptional in that they molt the flight feathers progressively and so never lose the ability to fly.

Male wildfowl tend to be brighter than the females, most of which require a drab plumage for camouflage when incubating eggs. However, if males were to retain a striking

Feeding techniques

Each species of duck, goose and swan uses one or more of three feeding methods: diving, dabbling at the water surface and grazing. True geese are generally less dependent on water than true ducks and swans. They feed mainly on land on grasses and grasslike plants, and their feeding grounds may be some distance from the nearest body of water. In winter flocks of geese commute between feeding areas, often farmland, and roosting areas, usually lakes and marshes. Crops such as potatoes, peas and turnips often feature in the diets of geese, which sometimes leads to conflict with farmers. Screamers graze lush sedges and grasses near to marshes.

Unlike mammals, vegetarian wildfowl lack gut-dwelling bacteria that can digest cellulose (the cell walls of plants). They gain nourishment from only the contents of the plant cells, and pass the undigested cellulose in their feces.

Breeding

Swans and true geese pair for life and the sexes tend to look similar. They build a substantial nest of twigs and aquatic vegetation at the water's edge or, in some species, in the form of a floating raft.

Most species of ducks stay with a mate for one season only, and display marked sexual dimorphism (different male and female plumages). Among the exceptions are the nine whistling ducks, in which the sexes are alike in appearance. Ducks are mainly ground-nesters, scraping depressions in the earth, between rocks and among dense undergrowth. They usually line these simple hollows with moss, rootlets and feather down. Some duck species nest in trees, using natural cavities in hollow trees and holes abandoned by large species of woodpecker. Hole-nesting species include the American wood duck (*Aix sponsa*), mandarin duck (*Aix galericulata*), goldeneye (*Bucephala clangula*) and common merganser (*Mergus merganser*). In some areas conservationists have provided artificial nestboxes for these species.

All wildfowl chicks are nudifugous, that is, they leave the nest almost immediately. They are covered with downy feathers upon hatching and can walk and swim within hours. The chicks of hole-nesting ducks must first leap to the ground, which may be a drop of as much as 50 feet (15 m).

Migration

A number of wildfowl are strongly migratory. Most of the gray geese (genus *Anser*) and black geese (genus *Branta*) breed in Arctic and subarctic latitudes, and in the fall fly south to spend the winter in the middle latitudes of the Northern Hemisphere. They follow well-defined flyways, stopping to rest and feed at traditional sites on the way. The tundra swan, *Cygnus columbianus*, known as Bewick's swan in Eurasia, and the trumpeter swan also migrate between the Arctic and warmer midlatitudes. The bar-headed goose, *Anser indicus*, migrates between its Tibetan breeding grounds and its winter home on the plains of India. To do so it must cross the Himalayas Mountains, flying to heights of almost 29,500 feet (9,000 m), higher than any other bird.

Wildfowl are strong fliers and include the fastest of all birds in steady, level flight. The long-tailed duck or old-squaw, *Clangula hyemalis*, has been recorded at 71 miles per hour (115 km/h) in level flight. The canvasback (*Aythya valisineria*), spur-winged goose (*Plectropterus gambiensis*) and red-breasted merganser (*Mergus serrator*) are also fast fliers. Ducks, geese and swans have large, well-developed pectoral (chest) muscles for powering the wings.

Relationship with humans

Ducks and geese were among the earliest birds to be farmed, for their eggs and meat. Captive herds of swan geese, *Anser cygnoides*, were kept in China over 2,000 years ago. Since then three other species of wildfowl have also been widely domesticated for their eggs and meat: the muscovy duck

Mallard ducklings attend their mother closely. She leads them to water shortly after they have dried out from hatching.

(*Cairina moschata*), greylag goose (*Anser anser*) and mallard (*Anas platyrhynchos*). Domesticated ducks and geese have very variable plumages and interbreed freely with wild birds.

The feathers of ducks and geese, especially the soft down from the breast, have long been used to line clothing and bedding. Eider feathers are valued highly, and are still gathered in Arctic Canada, Greenland and Iceland. If properly regulated, this is a sustainable harvest, because the eider feathers are taken from the snug linings of the birds' nests.

Conservation

Excessive hunting and the destruction and degradation of wetlands are the main threats facing ducks, geese and swans. The populations of many species have declined regionally, and today huge flocks of wildfowl are less common than in the past. The last labrador duck, *Camptorhynchus labradorius*, was shot in 1875, while four species of wildfowl became critically endangered during the 20th century: the crested shelduck (*Tadorna cristata*), of easternmost Asia and Japan, the pink-headed duck (*Rhodonessa caryophyllacea*), of India, the Brazilian merganser (*Mergus octosetaceus*) and the Madagascar pochard (*Aythya innotata*). A further two species are now endangered, and 19 more are considered to be vulnerable.

Wildfowl respond well to captive-breeding programs, however, and in this way conservationists have saved a number of species from almost certain extinction. By 1950 the population of the Hawaiian goose, or nene, *Branta sandvicensis*, was less than 50. This decline was due to hunting, the overgrazing of its habitat by livestock and heavy predation by non-native animals introduced to Hawaii. Intensive captive-breeding projects raised the total population to 2,000 within just 30 years, though the species is still classed as vulnerable.

For particular species see:
• BARNACLE GOOSE • CANADA GOOSE
• EIDER • GREYLAG GOOSE • HAWAIIAN GOOSE
• MALLARD • MERGANSER • MUSCOVY DUCK
• PINK-FOOTED GOOSE • PINTAIL • POCHARD
• SCREAMER • SHELDUCK • STEAMER DUCK
• STIFFTAIL • SWAN • TEAL • TORRENT DUCK
• WHISTLING DUCK • WOOD DUCK

Index

Page numbers in *italics* refer to picture captions.
Index entries in **bold** refer to guidepost or biome and habitat articles.

Page numbers in *italics* refer to picture captions. Index entries in **bold** refer to guidepost or biome and habitat articles.

719

Page numbers in *italics* refer to picture captions. Index entries in **bold** refer to guidepost or biome and habitat articles.